THE LATE PRECAMBRIAN GEOLOGY OF THE SCOTTISH HIGHLANDS AND ISLANDS

FRONTISPIECE: The Torridonian sandstone An Teallach range (1062m), rising above the irregular Lewisian basement, an old landscape formed in Stoer Group times. Stoer Group basal conglomerates occur in the valley bottom near the road bridge. Post glacial raised beaches are also visible (Locality 3, Itinerary X).

GEOLOGISTS' ASSOCIATION GUIDE

No. 44

THE LATE PRECAMBRIAN GEOLOGY OF THE SCOTTISH HIGHLANDS AND ISLANDS

By

M. J. Hambrey, I. J. Fairchild, B. W. Glover,

A. D. Stewart, J. E. Treagus and J. A. Winchester

Edited by C. J. Lister

1991

CONTRIBUTORS

I. J. Fairchild, School of Earth Sciences, University of Birmingham, P.O. Box 363, Birmingham B15 2TT.

B. W. Glover, Department of Geology, University of Keele, Keele, Staffordshire, ST5 5BG.

M. J. Hambrey, Scott Polar Research Institute, University of Cambridge, Lensfield Road, Cambridge CB2 1ER.

A. D. Stewart, formerly Department of Geology, University of Reading, Whiteknights, Reading, RG6 2AB. (Now: Paoluccio, 05020 Porchiavo del Monte, Italy).

J. E. Treagus, Department of Geology, University of Manchester, Manchester M13 9PL.

J. A. Winchester, Department of Geology, University of Keele, Keele, Staffordshire, ST15 5BG.

Notes. The details of routes given in this guide do not imply a right of way. The onus of obtaining permission to use footpaths and to examine exposures rests with the user of the guide, who should carefully observe the Code of Geological Fieldwork issued by the Geologists' Association (for address see inside front cover).

In particular, those in charge of parties should ensure that there is no indiscriminate hammering of, or collecting from, exposures and that no damage is caused to property.

Any information (e.g. change in footpaths, filling in of quarries, threat to SSIs, new exposures) that would update and improve a revised edition of this guide would be welcomed by the Association.

CONTENTS

Photographs were taken by M. J. Hambrey except where otherwise stated.

List of Figures

Tables

PREFACE

Most geological field excursion guides are of a regional character. The approach for this one is thematic. It aims to provide a broad picture of the Middle and Late Proterozoic evolution of Scotland by focussing principally on the character of the sedimentary rocks in order to recreate, as far as possible, the environments of deposition and their palaeotectonic setting.

Three main groups of rocks are the subject of this guide: the Dalradian Supergroup, the Moine Assemblage and the Torridonian complex. It is well known that the Torridonian represents the most spectacular development of sedimentary rocks in the British Isles, superbly displaying evidence of the character of the depositional environments. The Dalradian Supergroup is a metasedimentary sequence which in much of Scotland is highly deformed, but in recent years work on relatively undeformed rocks in the west has led to an excellent understanding of the evolution of the Dalradian basin prior to the Caledonian Orogeny. Even the largely high grade metamorphic rocks of the Moine Assemblage show many signs of their mode of deposition prior to deformation.

This guide, then, draws attention primarily to the sedimentary characteristics of the rocks. Structural aspects are considered mainly to provide the necessary background information in order to understand the disposition of the strata in any particular area. This is particularly true for the Dalradian and Moine rocks of the Highlands.

The guide covers a wide area geographically, from the islands off the west coast as far south as Islay, to the central Grampian Highlands and the North West Highlands as far north as the Lochinver district. Other guides cover some of these areas, but most of the information presented herein is new. The itineraries cover some of the most dramatic and rugged coastal and mountain scenery in the Scotland. The intense glacial erosion of the Pleistocene Epoch (ending about 10,000 yrs ago) steepened the valley sides and scoured the bedrock, creating large areas with excellent exposure.

The basis for this guide was an unpublished 10-day excursion guide for the 1985 Working Group meeting of Project 179 of the International Geological Correlation Programme: 'Stratigraphic methods as applied to the Proterozoic record'. The excursion organiser and compiler wishes to thank Dr. I. J. Fairchild (University of Birmingham), Dr. A. D. Stewart (University of Reading), Dr. J. E. Treagus (University of Manchester) and Dr. J. A. Winchester (University of Keele), not only for their contributions to the original guide and leading their respective parts of the excursion, but also for their willingness to undertake the necessary revision for this volume. Financial support for the original guidebook preparation from the Royal Society and the International Geological Correlation Programme is gratefully acknowledged. The editor also thanks Dr. A. C. M. Moncrieff for field and other assistance, together with Pat Hancock, Sheila Ripper (Department of Earth Sciences, University of Cambridge) and Carl Burness (University of Birmingham) who undertook much of the typing and drafting.

Michael J. Hambrey
(Cambridge, December 1989)

INTRODUCTION

Scope of guide

This guide is intended to provide an overall picture of the Proterozoic evolution as represented by the three contrasting sedimentary and metasedimentary sequences of Scotland: the Dalradian Supergroup, the Moine Assemblage and the Torridonian complex (Table 1). It includes some of the classic areas of British geology, as well as some equally interesting areas not widely known to geologists. An excursion over twelve days, linking all the itineraries described herein, furthermore takes one through some of Scotland's finest scenery, from the wind-swept islands off the west coast to the wooded glens of the Central Highlands, and on to the rugged, fjord-indented coastline and ice-sculptured mountains of the far north-west. Figure 1 shows the location of the individual itineraries.

The layout of this guide has been planned to describe the rocks in sequence from youngest to oldest. In detail this has not always been possible for simple reasons of geography or because of complex structural geology. The first rocks to be described are latest Proterozoic (Vendian) Dalradian rocks on the Garvellach Islands and the Isle of Islay (Lower Argyll-Upper Appin groups). These are relatively undeformed, and stratigraphic and sedimentological studies in the last 20 years or so have provided a fascinating story of evolution of the Dalradian basin, prior to the opening and subsequent closure of the Iapetus Ocean and the resulting Caledonian Orogeny. The guide then describes older Proterozoic (Riphean) rocks of the Appin Group in the Loch Leven and Schiehallion areas of the Central Highlands. These two areas show a marked contrast with each other, the latter being a much more attenuated and structurally complex sequence, preserving few sedimentary indicators. Moving east to the A9 road and then back west along by Loch Laggan the guide covers rocks of the Grampian Group, considered by some to be the lowermost of the Dalradian groups, with lower Appin Group rocks taken in *en route* as well.

Crossing the Great Glen Fault near Fort William we enter the Moine Assemblage, and several stops of sedimentological and structural interest are made in each of the main tectono-stratigraphic divisions of the Moines.

The remainder of the excursion concerns the Torridonian. These foreland rocks, dominated by continental clastic sediments, form spectacular mountains, which rise abruptly above the heavily ice-scoured surface of the Lewisian basement. The Torridonian sediments cover a pre-Torridonian hilly landscape which is often clearly visible. Three groups have been formally defined: the Torridon (youngest), Sleat and the Stoer groups. The Sleat Group is examined on

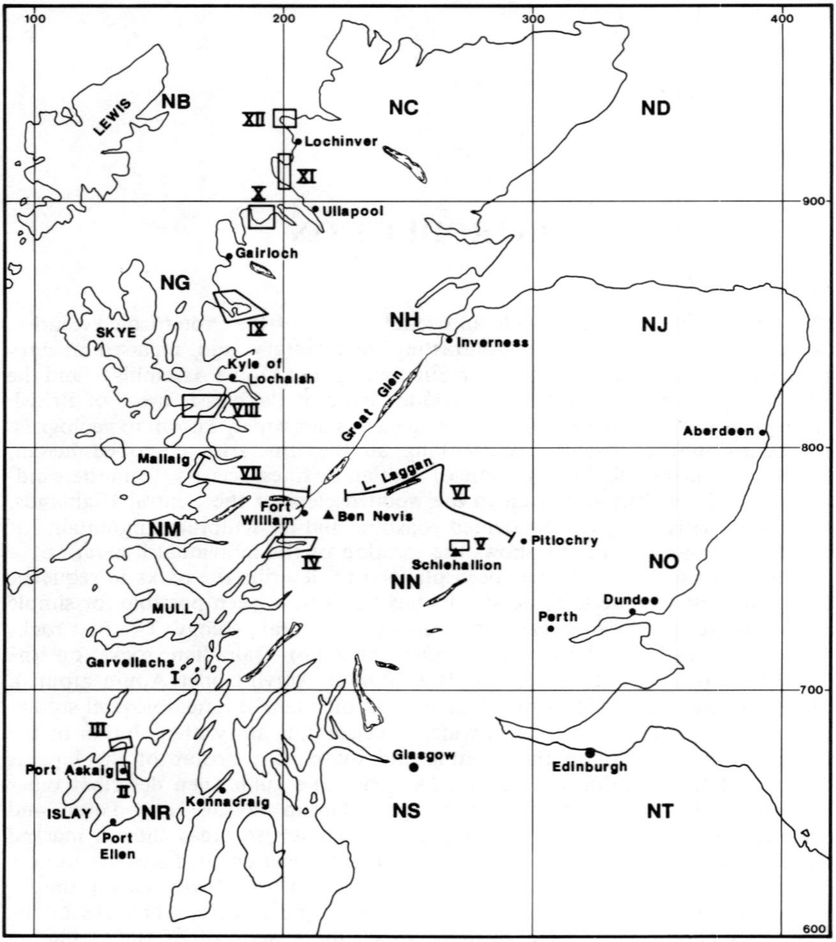

Figure 1. Location map of itineraries.

the Isle of Skye, the other two groups at various places between Loch Torridon and the Stoer Peninsula. Several of these mainland Torridonian localities were described by Stewart (in Barber *et al*, 1978), but revised and updated descriptions are included here.

Access

Each of the itineraries can be considered as a full day excursion. Public transport is inadequate for many of these itineraries.

AGE		HEBRIDEAN CRATON	CALEDONIDES		DEFORMATIONAL EVENTS
Ma			N.W.HIGHLANDS	CENT. HIGHLANDS	
510	ORDOVICIAN	Durness Group		S.Highland Gp.	← Caledonian
			Dalradian Super-group		← Grampian
570	CAMBRIAN			Argyll Gp.	
650				Appin Gp.	
800	NEO-PROTERO-ZOIC	Torridon Gp. Sleat Gp.		Grampian Gp.	
		Stoer Group		Central ? Highland Gp.	
1000			Loch Eil Div.		← Grenvillian ("Ardgourian")
	MESO-PROTERO-ZOIC	Moline Assemblage	Glenfinnan Div.		
			Morar Div.		
1500					
1600					} "Late" Laxfordian
2000	PALAEO-PROTERO-ZOIC	Loch Maree Gp. volcanics & sediments	?		Repeated deformation "Early" Laxfordian
		Scourie Dyke swarm	Lewisian Complex		
		Lewisian Complex	Lewisian Complex		← Inverian episode
2500		Loch Maree Group?			
	ARCHAEAN	Scourian Complex			← Badcallian episode
3000		Supra-crustal units			

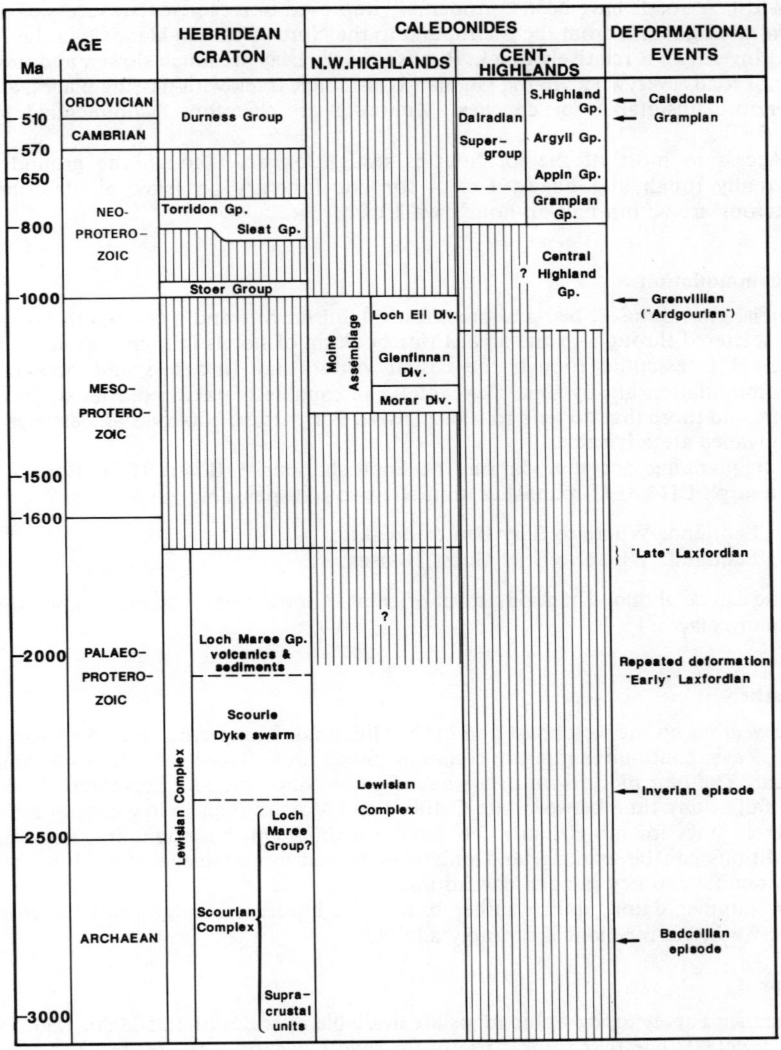

Table 1. Summary of Precambrian stratigraphic sequences in Scotland. The time-scale is a chronometric one, adopted by the International Union of Geological Sciences (IUGS, 1989); commonly used chronostratigraphic alternatives which are not well defined in a Scottish context, are Vendian and Riphean, which together partly overlap with Neoproterozoic. The terms Neo-, Meso- and Palaeoproterozoic are approximately equivalent to Late, Middle and Early Proterozoic.

Most 'A' roads have been considerably improved in recent years. Access to the Central Highlands from the South, and to the North-West Highlands (via the A9 and Inverness) is relatively quick. Roads towards Islay are much slower, and most minor roads everywhere in the Highlands are single track with passing places, and therefore unsuitable for coaches. Minibuses are therefore recommended for parties.

Access to most of the localities is straightforward, though the ground is normally rough and boggy. Except for one itinerary on Islay, all described outcrops are within half-an-hour's walk of a road.

Accommodation

Hotels, guest houses, bed-and-breakfast establishments and a few youth hostels are scattered throughout the area. Prior booking of hotels in high season (July-August) is essential though the casual visitor may find bed and breakfast accommodation at any time. Few hotels are capable of taking parties of 20 or more, and those that do tend to be expensive. For parties, bookings at least a year in advance are advisable.

For planning accommodation the Scottish Tourist Board (P.O. Box 707, Edinburgh EH4 3EU) publishes annually two indispensable guides:

'Scotland: Where to Stay Bed & Breakfast',
'Scotland: Where to Stay Guest Houses'.

These can be obtained at good, travel-orientated book shops. Camping is possible in many places.

Weather

The weather on the west coast and in the Highlands is unpredictable. High winds and heavy, continuous rain are common. Some areas have as much as 4000mm a year. The best months *on average* tend to be May-June and September. Snow can fall at any time between late October and May, though in low coastal areas it rarely stays for more than a few days at a time. On the mountains, however, conditions can be extreme, and only experienced mountaineers should venture into remote country in such conditions.

In summer damp, mild weather brings out hordes of midges and therefore effective insect repellant is strongly advised.

Maps

Ordnance Survey topographic maps are available at scales of 1:250,000, 1:50,000 and 1:25,000. The first is most useful for road navigation, the second and third for seeking out localities.

Geological Survey maps are mainly out of date or out of print, and for the purposes of this guide are not very helpful. Reference is made in the text to the most recent geological maps, published mainly in various geological journals. The Geological Survey 'Ten-Mile' Map, Sheet 1 gives a good overall view of the geology of the whole of Scotland.

Other geological guides

The following Geologists' Association guides cover overlapping areas to this guide, but are not restricted to Proterozoic rocks:

No. 13 Skye
No. 21 North-West Scotland
No. 35 Mallaig

Other relevant guides include:

Allison, I., May, F. & Strachan, R. A. 1988. *An excursion guide to the Moine geology of the Scottish Highlands*. Scottish Academic Press, 270pp.

Johnson, M. R. W. & Parsons, I. 1979. *Macgregor and Phemister's Geological Excursion Guide to the Assynt District of Sutherland*. Edinburgh Geological Society. 76pp.

Roberts, J. L. and Treagus, J. E. 1977. The Dalradian rocks in the North Ballachulish district. *Scottish J. Geol.* 13, 165-184.

Further reading

Craig, G. Y. (ed.) 1983. *Geology of Scotland*, 2nd edition, Scottish Academic Press, Edinburgh, 472pp.

Winchester, J. A. 1988. *Later Proterozoic stratigraphy in the Northern Atlantic Regions*. Blackie & Son, Glasgow, 288pp.

PROTEROZOIC EVOLUTION OF SCOTLAND

During the Proterozoic Eon, which lasted from about 2500 to 570 Ma ago, Scotland underwent a long and complex evolution (Table 1). The earliest rocks belong to the Archaean to early Proterozoic (Paleoproterozoic; IUGS 1989 time-scale) Lewisian Complex which characteristically are high grade metamorphics that have suffered polyphase deformation, and therefore preserve evidence of sedimentary evolution only in their mineralogy and geochemistry. They are not considered as part of this guide.

Middle Proterozoic (Mesoproterozoic; IUGS 1989) and late Proterozoic (Neoproterozoic) rocks are represented by three complexes: the Moine Assemblage, which although strongly deformed and metamorphosed, in part preserves good sedimentological features; the Torridonian, with its beautifully exposed and superbly displayed sedimentary structures; and the Dalradian with well-preserved sedimentary features in the west, though much more deformed in the main part of its outcrop. The Torridonian forms a cover sequence to the cratonic Lewisian Complex, whilst the Moines and Dalradian belong to the metamorphic Caledonides.

These different rock complexes may belong to different tectonic terranes, i.e. they were not juxtaposed as they are today. Rather they may have been widely separated, brought together in Late Caledonian time by major strike-slip movements that may have characterised part of the Orogen prior to Carboniferous time.

HEBRIDEAN CRATON

The Lewisian Complex was formed as part of the old Laurentian and Greenland Shield which includes rocks as old as 3800 Ma. This shield area, comprising continental crust was subject to several stages of reworking, recrystallization and accretion, Scotland recording the later stages of this period of evolution (Table 1). Most of the rocks were accreted from the mantle at c. 2900 Ma. A limited amount of younger reworked material is represented by the Scourie mafic dykes (c.2000-2400 Ma) and Laxfordian vein, sheet and dyke complexes. All these were formed at great depths in the crust. The only clear evidence of processes at the earth's surface comes from the younger metasedimentary and metavolcanic rocks of the Loch Maree Group, which consist mainly of a thick sequence of rift-related tholeiitic basalts and greywackes of early Proterozoic age (about 2000 Ma), deposited after the intrusion of the Scourie dykes.

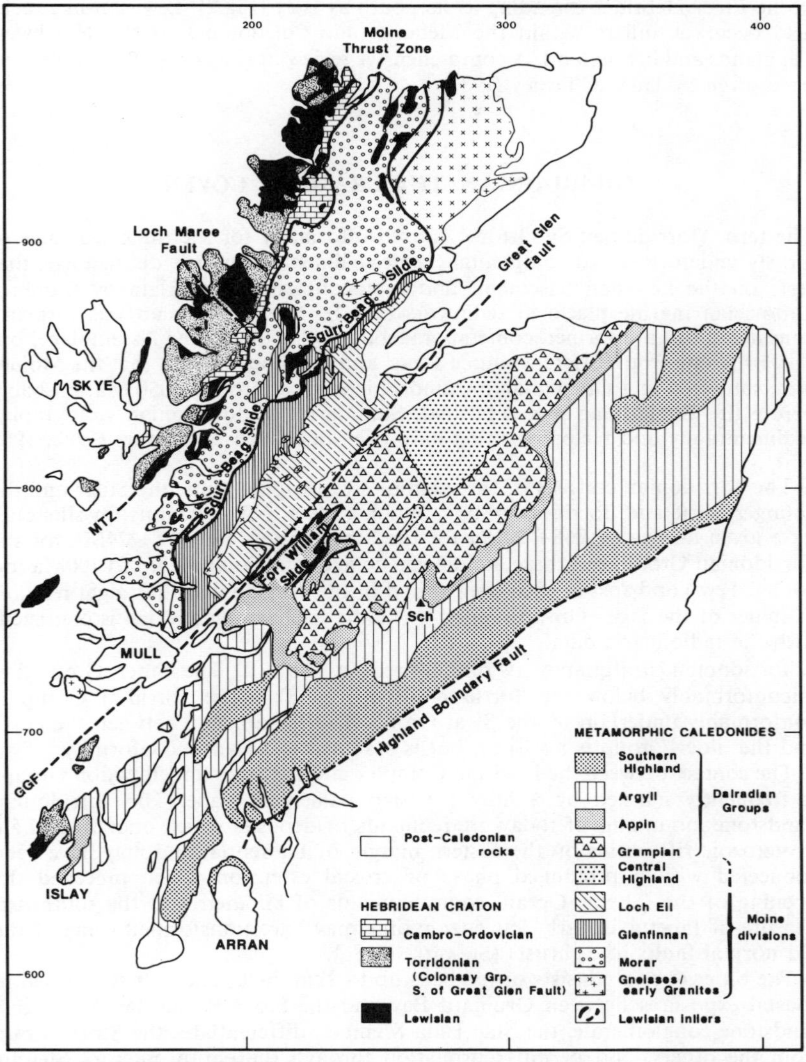

Figure 2. Distribution of Proterozoic rocks in Scotland, modified from Kelling *et al.* (1985) for Northern Highlands and Johnson (1983). Late Caledonian granites are omitted for simplicity.

Cratonic Lewisian rocks crop out mainly in a strip extending from the northwest tip of Scotland at Cape Wrath to the Isle of Skye, and in the Outer Hebrides, while further outcrops, tectonised during Caledonian Orogeny, occur in the Inner Hebrides extending as far south as Islay (Fig.2). Lewisian-like rocks also occur as inliers within the Metamorphic Caledonides of the Northwest Highlands and in Shetland. A comprehensive review of the Lewisian Complex has been given by Park & Tarney (1987).

TORRIDONIAN: THE CRATONIC COVER

The term 'Torridonian Sandstone' is used informally for the thick sequence of largely undeformed red continental clastic sediments of poorly defined age, that rests on the Lewisian basement, and is unconformably overlain by Cambro-Ordovician marine platform sediments (Fig.2). The Torridonian was formerly considered to have formed contemporaneously with the Moine Assemblage, but they originate from different source areas, and it is now thought that the Moines were subjected to a Grenvillian metamorphic event at around 1050 Ma, probably before the Torridonian was deposited. Summaries of Torridonian stratigraphy, sedimentology and tectonic setting have been published by Stewart (1982, 1988 a,b).

The Torridonian consists of three major stratigraphic units, the Stoer and the younger Sleat and Torridon groups. Whole-rock Rb-Sr isochrons on siltstones have given an age of 968 ± 24Ma for the Stoer Group and 777 ± 24Ma for the Torridonian Group, but these are diagenetic ages and could be up to 100Ma too young. Few good fossils have been found in the Torridonian, but algal remains in shales of the Stoer Group suggest a Middle Riphean age, which is consistent with the radiometric data.

Torridonian stratigraphy is summarised in Table 2. The Stoer Group lies unconformably below the Torridon Group. In Skye the Torridon Group is conformably underlain by the Sleat Group. The relationship between the latter and the Stoer Group is not seen, but is assumed to be an unconformity.

The contact between the Lewisian Complex and the Stoer and Torridon Groups is frequently marked by a hilly Lewisian palaeolandscape. The Torridonian Sandstone mountains of today are remnants of deposits which once filled Late Proterozoic rift basins on the eastern margin of Laurentia, and may have been connected with a prolonged phase of crustal extension which preceded the opening of the Iapetus Ocean, some hundreds of kilometres to the southeast. Closure of Iapetus in early Palaeozoic time may have transformed some of the old normal faults into thrusts (Stewart, 1988a).

The *Stoer Group* consists of red beds up to 2km thick, and is best exposed in coastal exposures between Gruinard Bay and the Stoer Peninsula. A volcanic sandstone-conglomerate, the Stac Fada Member, differentiates the Stoer Group from the others, and permits correlation through the entire outcrop. Stewart (1988b) identified a variety of facies in the Stoer Group: (i) breccias immediately overlying the hilly Lewisian landscape, probably representing fanglomerates. (ii) conglomerates representing braided river flood deposits, (iii) a variety of cross-bedded sandstones, some of braided river origin, others representing aeolian dunes; (iv) muddy sandstones formed in ponded mudflats, and (v) thin-bedded siltstones and fine sandstones of lacustrine origin.

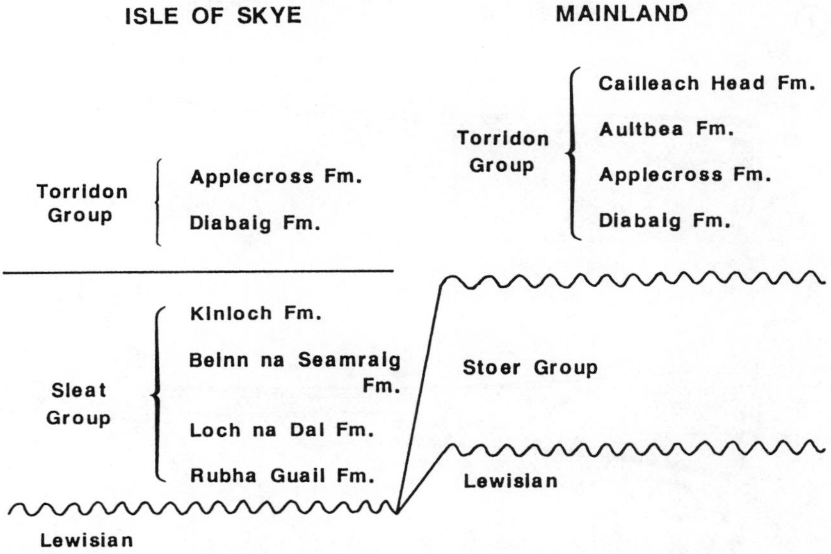

Table 2. Comparison of Torridonian stratigraphy between the Isle of Skye and the mainland of Northwest Scotland.

Palaeocurrents within the Stoer Group reverse through 180° twice at Stoer, suggesting fault-controlled deposition in a rift valley (Fig.3), and there are other indications of sharp disruption of depositional environments.

The *Sleat and Torridon groups* Stewart (1988a) form a conformable sequence probably about 200Ma younger than the Stoer Group. They appear to have originated during a later phase of extension across the same rift system in which the Stoer Group had been deposited (Fig.4). However, the younger sediments originated from a different source area under a much wetter climate. The Sleat Group is nowhere seen in contact with the Stoer Group, but in several localities an angular unconformity of 25° can be seen between the Stoer and Torridon groups. The unconformity between the Stoer and Torridon groups is represented by a rugged topography with palaeovalleys choked with Stoer sandstone detritus.

The *Sleat Group* comprises 3.5km of coarse grey fluviatile sandstones with subordinate grey shales. They are best exposed between Loch na Dal and Kylerhea (Itinerary VIII) on the Sleat Peninsula of Skye, where they occur within the Kishorn Nappe and conformably underlie the Torridon Group. Rocks resembling the Sleat Group do not occur outside the Kishorn Nappe, suggesting that they were deposited in an independent basin, the western edge being a listric normal fault which was reactivated as a thrust during the Caledonian Orogeny. The Sleat Group has been affected by greenschist facies metamorphism which has altered the colour from red to grey, but sedimentary structures are well preserved.

The stratigraphy of the Sleat Group with approximate thicknesses is as follows:

(iv) Kinloch Formation (1.2km) (top): strongly contorted cross-bedded

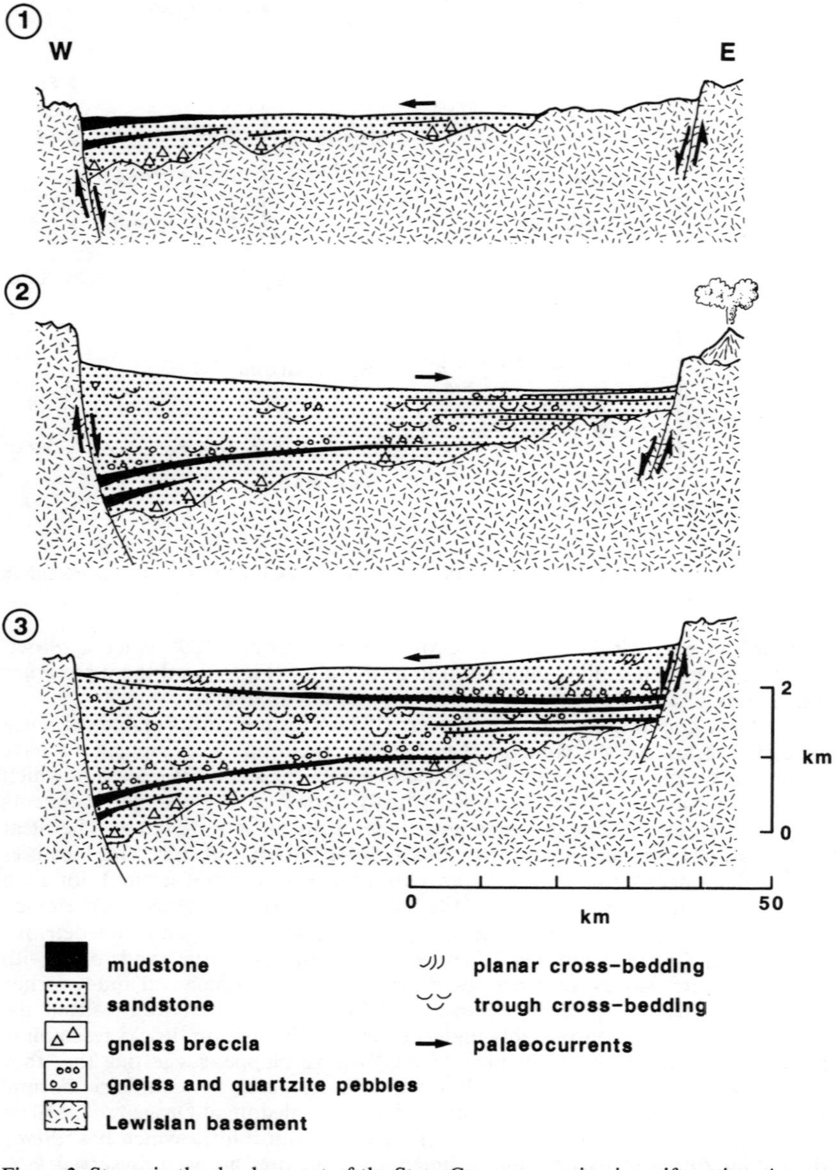

Figure 3. Stages in the development of the Stoer Group succession in a rift setting. Arrows indicate palaeocurrent directions. Stoer is located in the middle of the rift. (Reproduced from Stewart (1988b) with permission of Blackie & Son Ltd., Glasgow).

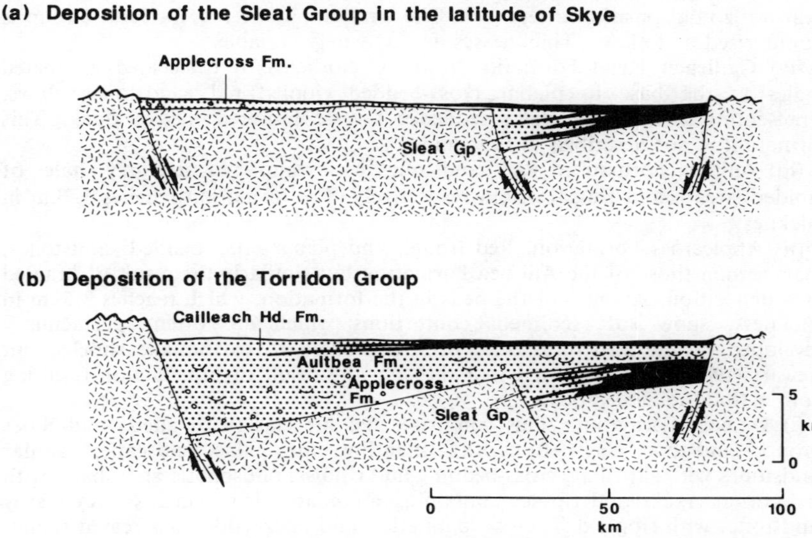

Figure 4. Stage in the development of the Sleat and Torridon groups, illustrating transverse profiles in the latitude of Skye, restored to show their configuration prior to Caledonian thrusting. (Reproduced from Stewart (1988a) with permission of Blackie & Son Ltd., Glasgow).

sandstones, with ripple-laminated horizons and minor shales, interpreted as a braided stream succession, with a source area to the west;

(iii) Beinn na Seamraig Formation (1.2km): Similar to the Kinloch Formation, but with palaeocurrents originating from the north and flowing parallel to the rift margin;

(ii) Loch na Dal Formation (0.8km): Trough cross-bedded fluvial sandstones in the upper part, with palaeocurrents from the west; alternating laminated siltstones (often phosphatic) and coarse sandstones representing a lacustrine fan toe sequence in the lower 200m;

(i) Rubha Guail Formation (0.3km): Coarse greenish trough cross-bedded sandstone and fine grained rippled and desiccated sediments, of fluvial and lacustrine origin respectively. The former become more dominant downwards towards a gneiss breccia which lies near the (unexposed) Lewisian unconformity. A westerly source is indicated.

The *Torridon Group* reaches 6km in thickness and rests on a Lewisian palaeoland surface (Frontispiece and cover with relief ranging from 600m near Loch Maree to almost nothing in the Cape Wrath area (Frontispiece and cover). Locally this former landscape has been exhumed by contemporary erosion. The Torridon Group is unconformably overlain by Cambro-Ordovician platform carbonates and quartzites. The flat-lying Torridon Group sediments were tilted prior to Early Palaeozoic deposition, then tilted back to their present generally near-horizontal position afterwards. The stratigraphy of the Torridon Group is summarised as follows. Thicknesses are extremely variable.

(iv) Cailleach Head Formation (top): Cyclothems of desiccated laminated shales at the base to planar cross-bedded rippled red sandstones above, representing a lacustrine-delta sequence several hundred metres thick. This formation is not described in this guide.

(iii) Aultbea Formation: Red sandstones with minor red and grey shales of braided stream and fluvial origin respectively. The formation reaches 1.5km in thickness.

(ii) Applecross Formation: Red trough and planar cross-bedded sandstones, coarser than those of the Aultbea Formation but similarly the result of braided river deposition. About half the beds in the formation, which reaches 3.5km in thickness, show soft sediment contortions which are often spectacularly developed. These structures have been attributed to earthquake shocks, but Stewart (1988a) has suggested that they are the result of liquefaction resulting from a flood-related process.

(i) Diabaig Formation: This comprises red breccias (with gneiss and Stoer Group sandstone clasts or both), mantling the palaeolandscape; tabular sandstones with silt films, cross-bedding and ripples; phosphatic grey shales with desiccation cracks and ripples containing abundant algal remains; grey clayey sandstones with ripple-drift cross-lamination and interbedded desiccated shales. This facies association represents a transition from fan deposits partially filling the palaeovalleys, through ephemeral lakes, to the arrival of Applecross braided rivers before the end of Diabaig Formation time. The formation is confined to the lower parts of palaeovalleys and has a maximum thickness of a few hundred metres.

Throughout Torridon Group time the main source area lay over Lewisian terrain to the west, beyond the margin of the major north-south-trending rift system.

In summary the late Proterozoic passive continental margin, which received the entire Torridonian succession, underwent syn-sedimentary fracturing due to lithospheric stretching parallel to the margin. The original normal faults are thought to have dipped eastwards, and may have been reactivated as thrusts during the Caledonian Orogeny (Stewart 1982, 1988b).

THE METAMORPHIC CALEDONIDES

The Hebridean craton is bordered to the east by the Moine Thrust Zone, where a series of thrust nappes involve both cratonic basement and cover (including Cambro-Ordovician sediments), and rocks of the Moine Assemblage.

To the east of the Moine Thrust Zone as far as the Great Glen Fault, the area is dominated by the older and most deformed rocks of the Metamorphic Caledonides, the Moine Assemblage of late Proterozoic (probably older Riphean) age. Between the Great Glen Fault and the Highland Boundary Fault, the area is made up principally of Riphean-Vendian metasediments of the Dalradian Supergroup, intruded by Late Caledonian granites (Fig. 2).

The Moine Assemblage

In the Northern Highlands, north-west of the Great Glen, the Moine Assemblage includes all Proterozoic rocks occurring east of the Moine Thrust (Fig. 2). Within this extensive area Moine rocks are in contact with inliers of 'Lewisian' basement rocks, and are overlain unconformably by Devonian 'Old Red Sandstone'.

The Moine Assemblage has not hitherto been described as a 'Supergroup' because the precise stratigraphic relationships of its constituent divisions are not yet fully established. Three Divisions are distinguished: the Morar Division in the west, the Glenfinnan Division, and the Loch Eil Division, which mostly abuts against the Great Glen Fault (Johnstone *et al.*, 1969). The entire area is structurally complex, with polyphase deformation and metamorphism, but all the Moine rocks of the Northern Highlands south of Ullapool occur within two major nappes, separated by a major ductile thrust: the Sgurr Beag Slide (Tanner, 1970). Overlying the Moine Thrust is the Moine Nappe: the Moine rocks within it are exclusively assigned to the Morar Division.

Overriding the Moine Nappe, its base formed by the series of ductile thrusts comprising the Sgurr Beag Slide Zone, is the Sgurr Beag Nappe. Within this nappe the stratigraphically lower semipelitic and psammitic gneisses form the Glenfinnan Division. They are overlain with apparent conformity by the dominantly psammitic rocks of the Loch Eil Division, distinguished from the Glenfinnan Division on purely lithological grounds (Fig.5).

Both the Morar Division and the Glenfinnan Division are in contact with 'Lewisian' basement slices. Interpretations of their mutual stratigraphic relationships vary, but the very large westward displacement on the Sgurr Beag Slide Zone inferred by chemical matching of amphibolites (Winchester, 1985) suggests that the Glenfinnan Division may be a distal lateral equivalent of the more proximal Morar Division. If so, the Loch Eil Division may either be the

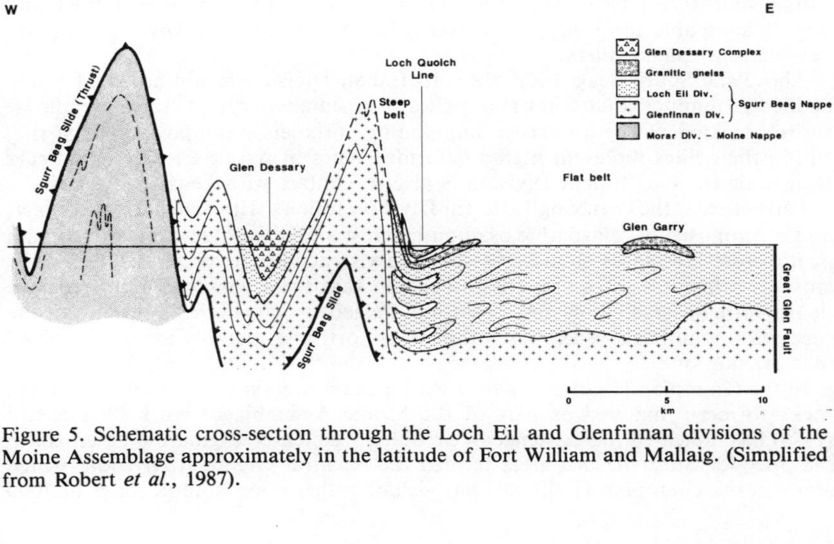

Figure 5. Schematic cross-section through the Loch Eil and Glenfinnan divisions of the Moine Assemblage approximately in the latitude of Fort William and Mallaig. (Simplified from Robert *et al.*, 1987).

lateral equivalent of the upper part of the Morar Division, or represent a higher stratigraphic level. Another interpretation is that the Moine sediments in the two nappes were deposited in separate basins simultaneously, and were later juxtaposed tectonically.

Roberts *et al.* (1987) recognised that the Glenfinnan (lower) and Loch Eil divisions were in stratigraphic continuity. However, their original relationship with the Morar Division is unknown, but could be a proximal equivalent of the structurally overlying divisions. These authors changed the divisions to group status.

The Moine Assemblage was originally correlated with the Torridonian, but radiometric dating from widely scattered localities east of the Moine Thrust Zone has indicated a metamorphic event around 1050 Ma. In each of the three Divisions north-west of the Great Glen, isotopic dates exceeding 1000 Ma have been obtained either from the metasediments or from metamorphosed igneous rocks which intrude the metasediments. There is a continuing debate concerning the significance of these data. However, this event would be equivalent to the Grenvillian Orogeny that is known from the Laurentian Shield and the southern Baltoscandian Shield. The Moine Assemblage is are therefore probably older than the Stoer Group, and was perhaps deposited as long ago as 1200-1300 Ma (Johnson, 1983). On the same basis the Moines are distinguished from the younger Proterozoic rocks of the Dalradian Supergroup.

Lithologically, the Moine Assemblage is a quite variable sequence of clastic sediments. Carbonates are exceedingly rare. Only the more competent psammitic rocks retain sedimentary structures. The Morar Division consists of alternating feldspathic psammites and pelites, with impure calc-silicate ribs developed. Sedimentary structures are abundant, and include cross-bedding, flaser bedding, ripple marks, slump folds and desiccation cracks. These indicate predominantly shallow water conditions, and palaeocurrent studies suggest dominant derivation from a southerly quarter. The Morar Division may be as much as 6km thick and several mappable units have been recognised (Table 3). The Division rests on Lewisian basement inliers.

Above the Sgurr Beag Slide, the Glenfinnan Division is composed of thinly bedded psammites, quartzites and pelites, but sedimentary structures are almost entirely lacking. Bodies of garnet-amphibolite of tholeiitic composition occurring within the pelites represent highly deformed relics of dykes. Close to the Sgurr Beag slide the Glenfinnan Division is also in contact with Lewisian rocks.

Further east, the overlying Loch Eil Division follows with transitional contact, and is composed of feldspathic psammitic schist and quartzite with relatively thin pelitic layers. In places abundant sedimentary structures are preserved, especially cross-stratification. Strachan (1986) believed that these rocks accumulated in a tidally-influenced, shallow marine setting. Palaeocurrents in the lower part of the succession mainly flowed towards the north-northeast, parallel to a coastline of that orientation.

In the Grampian Highlands recent work has resulted in a reappraisal of all the rocks formerly mapped as part of the Moine Assemblage. Work by Piasecki (1980) has indicated the existence of an older, frequently migmatitic basement in the Speyside-Strath Dearn area, termed the 'Central Highland Division' which alone in the Grampian Highlands has yielded rather poor isotopic dates of 1000

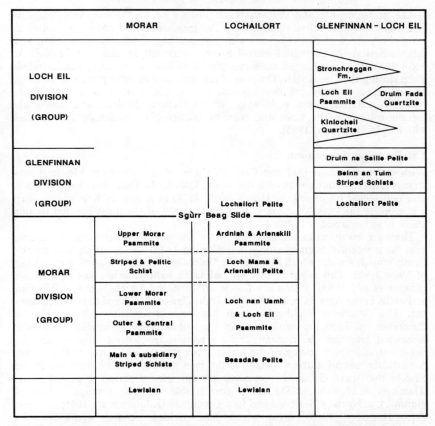

	MORAR	LOCHAILORT	GLENFINNAN – LOCH EIL
LOCH EIL DIVISION (GROUP)			Stronchreggan Fm.; Loch Eil Psammite / Druim Fada Quartzite; Kinlocheil Quartzite
GLENFINNAN DIVISION (GROUP)		Lochailort Pelite	Druim na Saille Pelite; Beinn an Tuim Striped Schists; Lochailort Pelite
Sgùrr Beag Slide			
MORAR DIVISION (GROUP)	Upper Morar Psammite	Ardnish & Arienskill Psammite	
	Striped & Pelitic Schist	Loch Mama & Arienskill Pelite	
	Lower Morar Psammite	Loch nan Uamh & Loch Eil Psammite	
	Outer & Central Psammite		
	Main & subsidiary Striped Schists	Beasdale Pelite	
	Lewisian	Lewisian	

Table 3. Stratigraphy of the Moine Assemblage of the Western Highlands (after Johnston, 1983; Roberts *et al.*, 1987).

Ma. Its geochemical signature is identical with that of the Glenfinnan Division of the Moine Assemblage in the Northern Highlands, and it is considered by some to be a portion of the Moine Assemblage cropping out southeast of the Great Glen. Others still question its existence, as its structural separation from the overlying rocks is not considered proven. Most of the rocks formerly mapped as Moine in the Grampian Highlands (the 'Younger Moines') have been shown to be in stratigraphic continuity with the Appin Group and have thus been renamed the Grampian Group by Harris *et al.* (1978), who considered it to be the lowest stratigraphic unit of the Dalradian Supergroup. However, some authors regard this designation as premature and retain the old term (e.g. Treagus 1987), while others consider the Grampian Group so unlike the overlying Dalradian groups that they favour its classification as a separate sequence below the Dalradian Supergroup.

The metamorphic and deformational history of the Moine Assemblage is complex. The Grenvillian ('Morarian') Orogeny around 1050Ma, resulted in at least two phases of deformation, with regional high-grade metamorphism and migmatisation. A pegmatite intrusive event occurred around 730 ± 20Ma. At 560 ± 10Ma the large Carn Chuinneag granite of Ross & Cromarty was intruded. Then during the Caledonian Orogeny there were several more phases of folding, accompanied first by the development of the Sgurr Beag Slide, high-grade regional metamorphism (c.450Ma) in the central Moines and low-grade metamorphism in the west, and then by retrogressive metamorphism around 440-400Ma (Johnson, 1983).

The Dalradian Supergroup

With the recognition that the Grampian Group (or 'Younger Moines') was stratigraphically continuous with the Appin Group, the Dalradian Supergroup is now considered by some (e.g. Harris *et al.*, 1978) to consist of four groups with a composite thickness of c.25km. The stratigraphy of the areas covered by this guide is summarised in Table 4.

There are few direct indicators of age in the Dalradian. However, the Palaeozoic ages have recently been questioned, following U-Pb dating of zircons on the Beinn Vuirich granite which intrudes the Dalradian Supergroup, and gives an age of 590 ± 2 Ma. This suggests that all Dalradian sedimentation was Proterozoic (Rogers *et al.*, 1989). Dalradian fossils are rare, but on the basis of Vendian acritarchs in the Argyll Group, the older Dalradian is considered to be of Riphean age. The Southern Highland Group has been described as having Lower Cambrian trilobites, acritarchs and in the northeastern Grampian Highlands somewhat debatable chitinozoans and a graptolite reputedly of Ordovician age, but the stratigraphic setting of the fossiliferous rocks is not certainly Dalradian. A particular useful marker horizon is the Port Askaig Tillite Formation at the base of the Argyll Group. It represents a major glacial period of global extent (Hambrey & Harland, 1985) and is correlatable with the Varanger tillites of Finnmark in Norway, Svalbard and East Greenland (Kilburn *et al.*, 1965; Spencer, 1975; Hambrey, 1983), areas which have yielded Vendian acritarchs. An interglacial shale in Finnmark has also provided a Rb-Sr whole-rock age of 654 ± 23 Ma (Pringle, 1973, new constants) this being considered the best indication of the age of tillites. However, in Scotland, the position of the Proterozoic-Cambrian boundary is poorly constrained; according to Anderton (1982) it is most likely to lie near the base of the Tayvallich Volcanics in the uppermost part of the Argyll Group (Table 4), but previous authors have preferred a lower level in that Group. Most recently, Halliday *et al.* (1989) have obtained a U-Pb zircon age for the Tayvallich Volcanics of 595 ± 4 Ma, thereby putting this formation in the Proterozoic Eon.

Dalradian sedimentation

Whether or not the Grampian Group is considered to be the lowest unit of the Dalradian Supergroup, its relationships with both the underlying Central Highland Division and the overlying Appin Group vary from stratigraphic to tectonic. Piasecki (1980) claimed that the Grampian Group rests unconformably

AGE		GROUP	SUBGROUP	ISLAY TO LOCH LEVEN [1,2]	SCHIEHALLION DISTRICT [3]	LOCH LAGGAN DISTRICT [4,5]	DRUMOCHTER TO STRATHTUMMEL
NEOPROTEROZOIC / LATE PROTEROZOIC	CAMBRIAN?	Southern Highland		Loch Avich Lavas Loch Avich Grits			
	"VENDIAN"	Argyll	Tayvallich	Tayvallich Limestone & Volcanics			
			Crinan	Crinan Grits			
			Easdale	Craignish Phyllites Easdale Slates Scarba Conglomerate			
			Islay	Jura Quartzite Bonahaven Dolomite] III Port Askaig Tillite] I & II	(14) Schiehallion Quartzite (13) Schiehallion Boulder Bed		
	?	Appin	Blair Atholl	Islay Limestone Mullach Dubh Phyllite Lismore Limestone Cuil Bay Slate	(12) Pale Limestone (11) Banded Group (10) Strath Fionan Dark Schist and Limestone Formation		
			Ballachulish	Appin Phyllite Appin Limestone Appin Quartzite Ballachulish Slate	(9) Strath Fionan Limestone (8) Strath Fionan Banded Fm. (7) Meall Dubh Quartzite (6) Meall Dubh Graphitic Schist		
	"RIPHEAN"		Lochaber	Ballachulish Limestone IV Leven Schist Glen Coe Quartzite Binnein Schist Binnein Quartzite Eilde Schist Eilde Quartzite	(5) Meall Dubh Limestone V (4) Meall Dubh Striped Pelite (3) Beoil Schist (2) Beoil Quartzite (1) Pelite and semipelite Quartzite	Kinlochlaggan Limestone Pelite and semipelite Kinlochlaggan Boulder Bed] VI Pelite and semipelite Kinlochlaggan Quartzite Semipelite and psammite Quartzite	----------*Boundary slide*---------- Beoil Schist Beoil Banded Quartzite & Schist Lower Beoil Banded Quartzite
		Grampian	Glen Spean	Eilde Flags [Inverlair Fm. Clachaig Fm.	Struan Flags	Inverlair Formation Clachaig Formation	Strathtummel Succession Drumochter Succession] VI
			Corrieyairack			Creag Meagaidh Fm. VI Ardair Formation Glen Doe Formation Coire nan Laogh Semipelite	
						slide	

Table 4. Composite stratigraphic successions in the Dalradian Supergroup. Roman numerals refer to Itineraries.

upon previously-metamorphosed Central Highland Division rocks (Moine), although the nature of the contact is usually obscured by a tectonic dislocation, the Grampian Slide. However, as yet no clear structural evidence that the Central Highland Division underwent earlier deformation has been documented. At the base of the Grampian Group succession in the Speyside area, a sporadically developed sequence of mixed limestones, quartzites and semipelites (the Ord Ban Subgroup) contains sheared pegmatites yielding ages extending back to 718 ± 19 Ma. (Piasecki and van Breemen, 1979). As the intrusion of the pegmatites must postdate deposition, and the dates yielded are similar to those of the 'Morarian' event of the Northern Highlands, the deposition of the Grampian Group must precede any such late Precambrian event which may have occurred. However, the Grampian Group also appears to have conformable upper contacts with the overlying Appin Group, although in the northwest contacts are usually sharp and highly strained and some formations appear to be missing owing to the proximity of the Fort William Slide.

The Grampian Group provides evidence of considerable thickness variations (Fig. 6). In the Atholl area its thickness may exceed 8 km, while near the Corrieyairach Pass the total thickness may be less than 3 km. Throughout the area a lower succession, characterised by deep water turbiditic sedimentation (the Corrieyairach Subgroup) is overlain by a fluviodeltaic sequence (the Glen Spean Subgroup) which records progressive filling of the Grampian Group basin by sediment derived from the south and west. Rapid local thickness variations and facies changes record syn-sedimentary faulting during the development of the Grampian Group basin. The succeeding Appin Group appears to record the onset

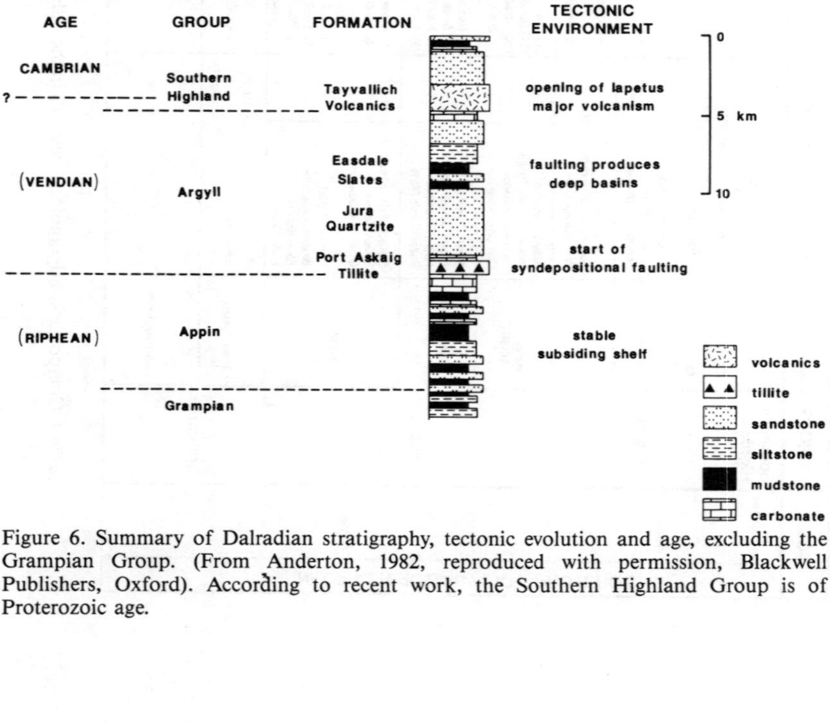

Figure 6. Summary of Dalradian stratigraphy, tectonic evolution and age, excluding the Grampian Group. (From Anderton, 1982, reproduced with permission, Blackwell Publishers, Oxford). According to recent work, the Southern Highland Group is of Proterozoic age.

of renewed subsidence, suggesting that the Grampian Group was a precursor to the main Dalradian basin (Fig. 6). For this reason, and because of the lithological and geochemical similarities of the Grampian Group to rocks of the Moine Assemblage, its inclusion within the Dalradian Supergroup is not universally accepted.

Anderton (1985) has provided a useful summary of depositional environments in the rest of the Dalradian Supergroup (summarised in Fig.7a). The lowest of the three subgroups of the Appin Group, the Lochaber, consists (in terms of original sediments) of several sand and muddy units. The sands can be interpreted as tidal-shelf deposits from their cross-bedding characteristics, whilst the muds indicate deeper water, low energy, shelf conditions. By analogy with modern tidal shelves a northeastwards-opening gulf with roughly Caledonoid-trending coastlines, and a sediment source either in the land mass to the northwest (Laurentia) or in the southwest at the head of the gulf is envisaged. Such conditions may have prevailed for much of Appin and Argyll group times. A short-lived glacial episode is suggested by the Kinlochlaggan Boulder Bed, an event not easily correlated with other parts of the Caledonides. At the top of the Lochaber Subgroup, the Ballachulish Limestone (placed by some, including Anderton, in the overlying Subgroup), indicates the onset of anoxic basin conditions. Such conditions continued into the Ballachulish Subgroup, but tidally influenced sedimentation returned, followed by renewed transgression and deposition of shelf carbonates. The Blair Atholl Subgroup comprises two mud-carbonate rhythms. The lowest

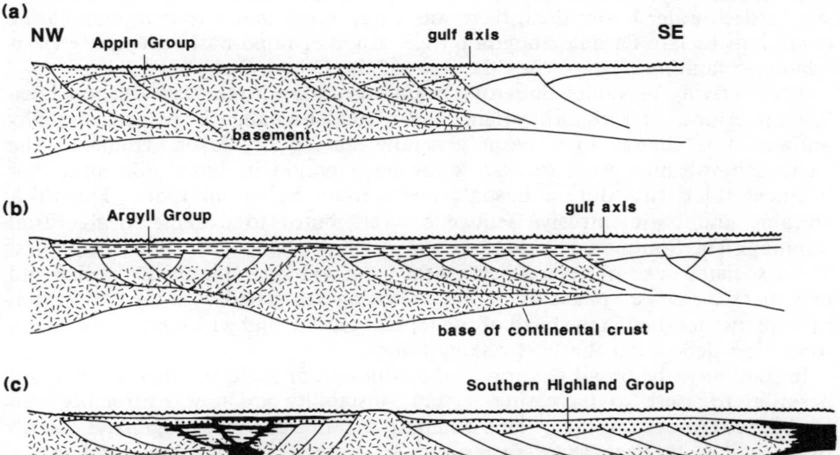

Figure 7. Schematic cross-sections through the Dalradian depositional basin in the SW Highlands during (a) late Appin Group time, (b) Argyll Group (Crinan Subgroup) time (and Southern Highland Group time). Basaltic intrusions and volcanics are shown in black. (From Anderton, 1985, reproduced with permission of Scottish Academic Press, Edinburgh).

rhythm suggests deep deoxygenated water, whereas the upper rhythm, including the Islay Limestone, contains stromatolites and associated facies indicating very shallow to intertidal conditions, especially at the top.

The Islay Subgroup is the lowest of the Argyll Group and begins with the Port Askaig Tillite Formation. This unit was deposited by an ice sheet of considerable extent that fed the basin with far-travelled material from the southeast. Bounding formations indicate arid, possibly warm climates, suggesting sharp climatic changes, a characteristic already well-established for the correlative tillites of Svalbard and East Greenland (Fairchild & Hambrey, 1984). A variety of depositional conditions, from grounded to floating ice are recorded in the Port Askaig Tillite (Spencer, 1971; Eyles, 1989). The Tillite is a useful marker horizon throughout the length of the Dalradian outcrop; for example, the Schiehallion Boulder Bed in Perthshire or the Claggan Boulder Bed in Connemara is a correlative. Normal shelf conditions returned after the ice-retreated, and a mixed clastic-carbonate sequence was deposited. This, the Bonahaven Dolomite, includes Britain's best Precambrian stromatolites, formed in a supratidal to subtidal environment, influenced by storms. Tidal-shelf conditions of the Jura Quartzite indicate uplift of a nearby source area combined with a tectonically induced marine transgression, though the palaeogeography still resembled that of Appin Group times.

Subsequent Dalradian evolution is not covered by this guide but may be summarised briefly. The transition into the Easdale Subgroup is represented by fault-related sedimentation and the first rapid deepening event in the Dalradian. As the deep water basin filled, there was a return to shallow to marginal marine conditions by late Easdale Subgroup time. Another rapid basin-deepening event related to faulting characterises the base of the Crinan Subgroup.

The overlying Tayvallich Subgroup begins abruptly with the Tayvallich or Loch Tay Limestone, of turbiditic origin, and a sudden change in palaeogeography initiated this change to a basin generally starved of clastic sediment. The Tayvallich volcanics were formed following a period of basic volcanism that intruded thick sills during Easdale and Crinan Subgroup times. The thick volcanic and basic intrusive sequence is attributed to extreme local crustal thinning. The Southern Highland Group consists almost entirely of turbidites. The associated lavas of Loch Avich are the most widespread in the Dalradian and may mark a renewed phase of crustal stretching associated with the continental rupture that resulted in the birth of the Iapetus Ocean, and which may have begun soon after deposition the Port Askaig tillites.

In summary, the broad features of the evolution of the Dalradian sedimentary basin in response to increasing tectonic instability are now reasonably well established (Anderton, 1985). This instability is reflected in the progressive change from shallow to deep water facies and an increase in volcanism, and was a response to stretching of the lithosphere.

Although the vertical succession of facies shows common characteristics throughout the Dalradian terrain, many stratigraphic units show significant lateral facies and thickness variations, reflecting differential subsidence and uplift of small fault blocks defined by Caledonoid-trending listric normal faults and faults at right angles to these (Fig. 7b) (Anderton, 1985). Thus the Dalradian does not exhibit a 'layer-cake' stratigraphy. The Caledonoid-trending (northeast-southwest) basin axis gradually shifted southeast southeast with time and incipient rifting took place, but was apparently aborted. The lithosphere eventually split some distance to the southeast of the Dalradian basin, creating in early Cambrian time the Iapetus Ocean (Anderton, 1985). An alternative model of Dalradian evolution was proposed by Graham (1986), who considered that the presence of tectonic features cutting across the Caledonoid trend were indicative of a transcurrent pull-apart basin.

Whichever model is correct, the subsequent Caledonian structural evolution of the Dalradian, following closure of Iapetus in Arenig time, may have been controlled, at least in part, by the tectono-sedimentary setting of the Dalradian sediments.

Influence of Caledonian Orogeny on the Dalradian Supergroup (J. E. Treagus)

The earliest deformation (D_1) to affect the Dalradian Supergroup resulted in three major folds, the Islay Anticline, Loch Awe Syncline and Tay Nappe (anticline), probably in a fan-like upward-facing arrangement as shown in Figure 8a. The rocks of Islay and of the west side of the Loch Leven district illustrate the upward-facing and low-grade metamorphic conditions on the northwestern side of this structure, whilst those in the Kinloch Laggan district probably represent deep levels in the central synclinal zone. The right way up, southeast-

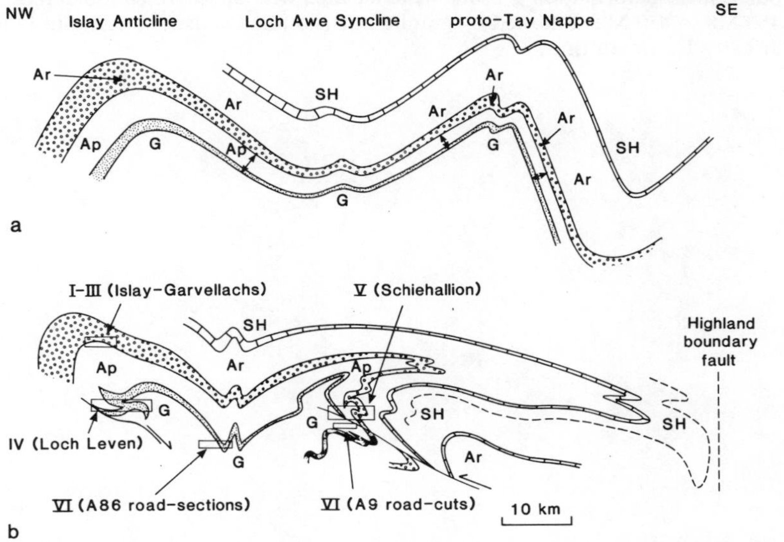

Figure 8. Structural development of the Dalradian Supergroup during the Caledonian Orogeny. (a) Possible original geometry of the D_1 folds (after Treagus, 1987). (b) Generalised cross-section of the present geometry of the Dalradian. The position of rocks seen in Itineraries I to VI is indicated. Groups are indicated as follows: G=Grampian, Ap=Appin, Ar=Argyll, SH=Southern Highland. The Lochaber, Islay and Tayvallich Subgroups are ornamented.

younging sequence of the Schiehallion district, according to Treagus (1987), represent rocks on the southeast limb of the (proto) Tay Nappe. The high-grade metamorphic rocks of the latter area preserve the fine-grained D_1 fabric as inclusions in porphyroblasts and exhibit refolded D_1 fold closures.

However, this south-eastern anticline representing the proto-Tay Nappe was subsequently affected by penetrative D_2 movements. These movements gave rise to the inverted disposition and southeast-facing of the lower limb of the present Tay Nappe, as seen in the A9 road localities (Itinerary VI) the southeast side of the Schiehallion district (Itinerary V; see Inset to Fig. 26), and in all the rocks between the Highland Boundary Fault and Schiehallion (see Fig. 8b). The deep burial of the rocks at this time, according to Dewey and Shackleton (1984) due to the emplacement of a giant ophiolite nappe, was responsible for the metamorphic conditions seen in the Schiehallion area, as well as in the exposures along the A9 and A86 sections and in the east of the Loch Leven district.

D_2 and subsequent deformations have modified the whole orogenic belt, causing the Islay Anticline to become more inclined and the D_1 folds in the Appin and Grampian Groups at Loch Leven to be refolded (Figure 8b). D_2 is also associated with northwest-directed thrusts (slides) on or near the Grampian/Argyll Group boundary. D_2 deformation has been shown to pre-date a granite near Pitlochry, the age of which is 514 ± 7 Ma (Bradbury *et al.*, 1976). Subsequent deformation is probably associated with uplift which took place from 460 Ma to 410 Ma, followed by granite intrusion and sinistral strike-slip faulting in early Devonian time.

ITINERARY I

Port Askaig Formation (Argyll Group) and topmost Islay Limestone (Appin Group) on the Garvellach Islands

I. J. FAIRCHILD

Maps: Ordnance Survey 1:50,000 sheet 55.
Geological: Spencer, 1971a, Plate 11.

Itineraries I, II and III concern some of the less-deformed Dalradian metasediments which are superbly exposed on Islay and the Garvellachs, offshore Argyll. They include the Port Askaig Tillite Formation and the carbonate-dominated sediments which bound it above and below (Table 5). Most of the interest centres on outcrop-scale sedimentology, but structural and petrographic features and the larger-scale sedimentation patterns are mentioned where appropriate. The Garvellachs excursion is placed first because here are the best exposures of the Port Askaig Formation.

The localities in excursions I to III can be combined with excursion guides previously published on other islands and the adjoining mainland to give a fuller picture of later Dalradian sedimentation: Anderton (1977, 1979) for facies and lateral variations on Jura; Roberts (1977), for Southern Highland Group lithology and structure on Kintyre; Gower (1977), for the Tayvallich Lavas and Limestone in the type area; Baldwin & Johnson (1977), for upper Argyll Group sedimentology on Lunga, Luing and Shuna. Other localities detailed in research publications are those of the Craignish Phyllites on Islay and the mainland

GROUP	FORMATION
Southern Highland	
Argyll	Jura Quartzite (5000m) Bonahaven Dolomite (300m) Port Askaig Tillite (750m)
Appin	Islay Limestone (250m)
Grampian	

Table 5. Summary Dalradian stratigraphic table with the formations seen on Itineraries I to III.

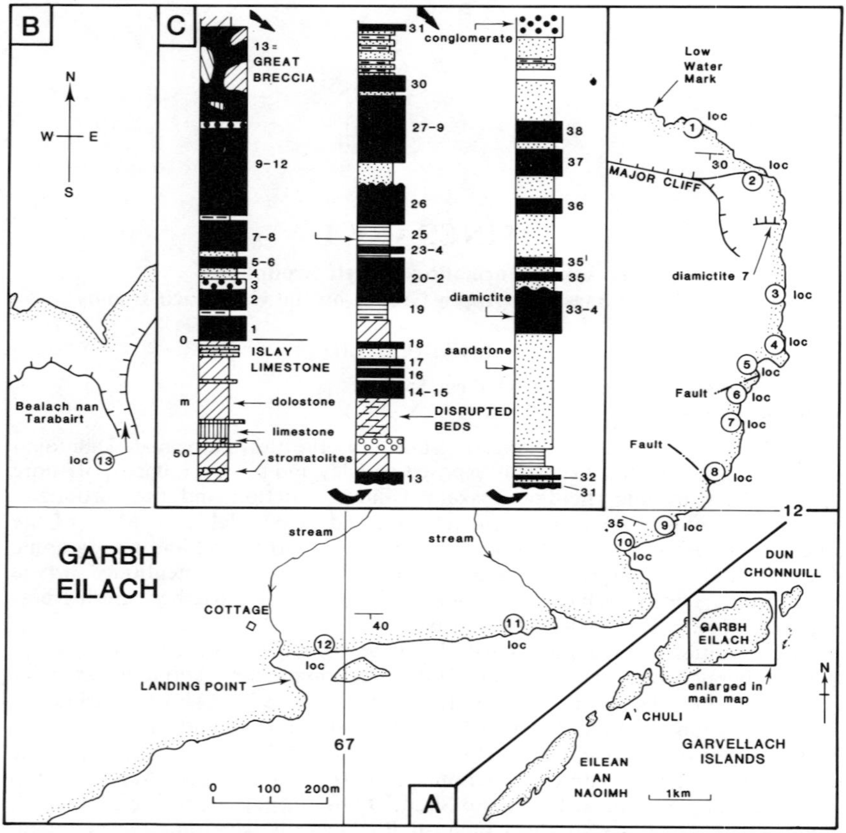

Figure 9. Itinerary I. A. Location of the Garvellach Islands. B. Locality map for Garbh Eilach. C. Summary stratigraphy of exposed Port Askaig Tillite and underlying Islay Limestone. Numbers to the right of the stratigraphic columns are bed numbers of diamictites. Information largely from Spencer, 1971a, with revised coastal outline.

(Anderton, 1975) and Proterozoic metasediments of uncertain affinity in western Islay (Stewart & Hackman, 1973; Fitches & Maltman, 1984).

The Garvellachs ('Isles of the sea') are a group of uninhabited islands in the Firth of Lorne exposing a uniformly-dipping 600m-thick succession which represents the most outstanding pre-Pleistocene glacial locality in the British Isles. They can be reached by chartering a small boat from Seil or Luing, easily accessible by road from Oban. The recommended boatman is Lachlan MacLachlan of Cullipool, Luing (Telephone Luing 282) who will also be able to advise about availability of simple accommodation in the cottage on the main island Garbh Eilach (Fig. 9). Camping is possible on each of the four main islands. The following itinerary assumes only a day visit.

Sedimentology of the Port Askaig Tillite Formation

The magnificent memoir by Spencer (1971a; still purchasable from the Geological Society of London) on the glacial sediments of the Dalradian is largely based on the outcrops of the Garvellachs together with those of Islay (Itinerary II). His stratigraphic work (Fig. 9) is a development of Kilburn, Pitcher & Shackleton (1965) and can be demonstrated with confidence because of the uniform dip and paucity of faulting on the Garvellachs. There is a large number of laterally continuous beds of diamictite ('mixtite' of Spencer, 1971a): poorly sorted admixtures of gravel, sand and mud-grade material. In the lower half of the Port Askaig Formation, the 'interbeds' which separate the diamictites are dolomitic (conglomerates, sandstones and mudrocks), which relates to the dominance of dolostone clasts in diamictites. In the upper half of the Formation there is a dominance of feldspathic igneous lithologies in the gravel fraction of diamictites and the interbeds are variably feldpathic sandstones (quartzites). Spencer (1971a, 1975) developed a model for glacial deposition (Fig. 10A) interpreting the diamictites as originally melt-out tills from grounded-ice around sea-level. Succeeding development of terrestrial periglacial conditions was inferred by the interpretation of polygonal patterns of sand wedges penetrating diamictites as patterned ground. These are often capped by a lag conglomerate (?beach) which

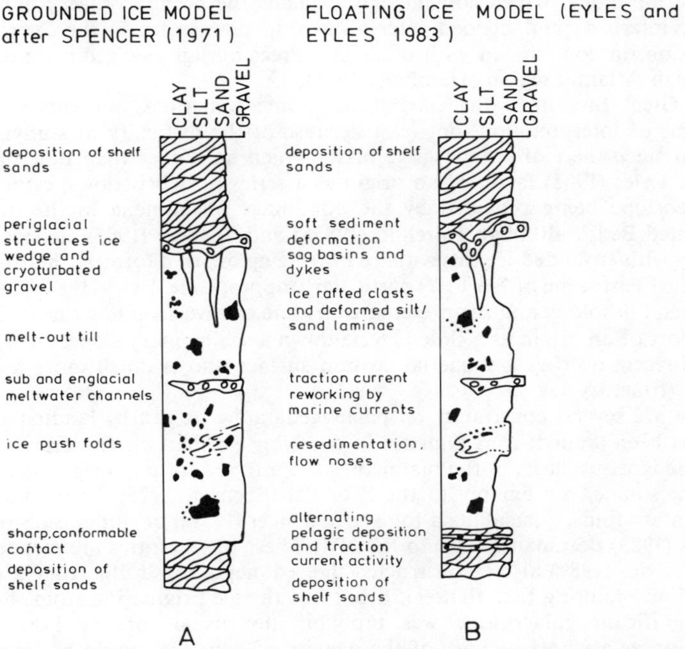

Figure 10. Itineraries I and II. Comparison of two models for cycles in the Port Askaig Tillite Formation (after Eyles and Eyles, 1983).

passes up into the shallow marine interbed. Many other features were recognized, notably graded laminites (interpreted as varves) and other laminated deposits with outsized clasts, many of which are demonstrably dropstones deposited from floating ice.

The main challenge to Spencer's work in the 1970's was provided by Schermerhorn (1974, 1975) who regarded the diamictites of the Port Askaig Formation and other late Precambrian alleged glacigenic sequences as deposits of sediment-gravity flows triggered by tectonic uplift. Syn-sedimentary faulting is indeed a feature of Anderton's (1985) model of basin evolution. However, the case for extensive glaciation at several times in late Precambrian time has continued to strengthen (Hambrey & Harland, 1981; 1985).

Increasing knowledge of Pleistocene and contemporary glacial facies associations allowed Eyles & Eyles (1983) and Eyles, Eyles & Miall (1985) to develop a new model for the Port Askaig Formation (Fig. 10B) in which shallow marine deposition and reworking and glaciomarine deposition from floating ice interrupted each other. Eyles & Clark (1985) strengthened this view by reinterpreting the sand wedges (said to be typically randomly- not polygonally-arranged) as injection features related to soft-sediment deformation of diamictites and overlying sands, as a consequence of gravitational instability related to coarsening-upwards of matrix. Eyles (1989) gave a fuller exposition of the glacimarine model which convincingly explains the peculiarly large number of tabular interbeds and bedded intervals within diamictites in the Port Askaig Formation, in comparison with other late Precambrian glacigenic sequences in the North Atlantic region (Hambrey, 1983).

The Great Breccia of the Garvellachs, some 40m thick, presents particular problems of interpretation, not least because of the difficulty of studying it at outcrop since there are many large clasts which are larger than outcrop-scale! Eyles & Eyles (1983) favoured an origin as a series of debris flows, evidence for a palaeoslope being provided by the boudinage phenomena in the overlying 'Disrupted Beds', although Fairchild (1985a) and Spencer (1985) considered the analogy with grounded-ice tills with ice moving up out of a formerly marine basin (as in the Pleistocene of Norfolk) particularly appropriate. Eyles (1989) cited both the general lithology and the presence of a zone of inverse grading near the base in support of an origin as a slide breccia down a sedimentary slope. On Islay the Great Breccia overlies a subaerial erosion surface and is much more texturally mature (Itinerary II).

There are several constraints on palaeogeography. A nearby landmass to the NW has been argued from evidence in overlying Formations (Itineraries II and III). The igneous clasts in the diamictites are inferred to have originated from a different source, presumably to the S or SE (Spencer, 1975; Anderton, 1982). Sedimentary folds, 'glacial push-folds' of Spencer (1971a) or slump folds of Eyles & Eyles (1983) dominantly face to the NW. These observations are reconciled in Fig. 11. Eyles (1989) also reconstructed the sedimentation in the context of syn-depositional faulting (her figure 15), but has the ice originating from the NW.

A significant palaeoslope was probably not usual for the Port Askaig Formation as a whole because of the paucity of beds that could be interpreted as sediment gravity flows; the dominant sedimentary structures in interbeds are cross-stratification (including sets up to several metres high in both conglomerates

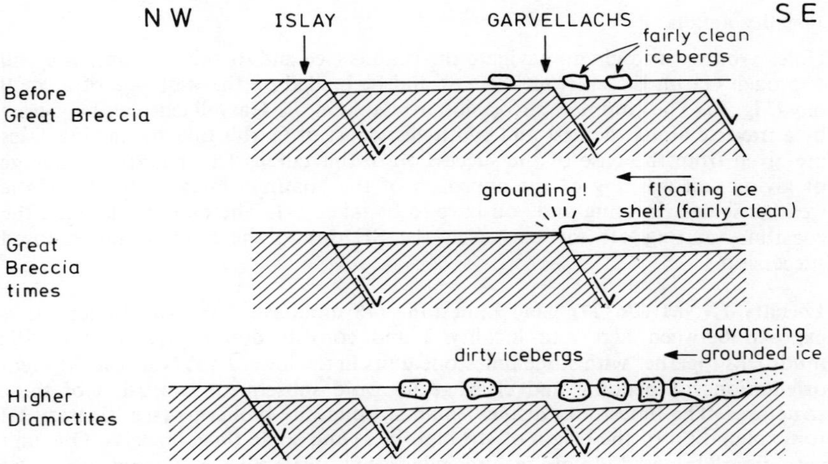

Figure 11. Itineraries I and II. Palaeogeographical cartoons for deposition of the Port Askaig Tillite Formation on a model assuming the floating ice origin of most diamictites, but the grounded ice origin of the Great Breccia.

and sandstones), and wave-rippling. Eyles (1989) attributed the sandstones, which dominate the interbeds, to a tidal-shelf regime of sedimentation.

Overall the special importance of floating ice as a depositional agent has been established, although many outcrop-scale features and lateral changes still defy detailed explanation and modes of deposition of individual beds can be debated.

In detail, the interbeds are more difficult to place in a clearly defined facies setting, representing only snapshots of rapidly changing sedimentary regimes and lacking diagnostic lateral changes that could be used in facies modelling. They have also failed to yield palaeoclimatic information. Whereas in NE Spitsbergen, carbonates within and bounding the two late Precambrian glacial formations clearly originated in different climatic regimes (Fairchild & Hambrey, 1984), the information in Scotland is equivocal. Most of the carbonate within the Port Askaig Formation is clearly detrital, but metamorphic recrystallization has obscured the origin of some of the carbonates. The situation is particularly tantalizing around the base of the Formation. Good evidence for active evaporation, and inferentially a warm climate, is provided by oolitic carbonates with fibrous cements near the top of the Islay Limestone on Islay and (less certainly) by the regular stromatolite bioherms on the Garvellachs. Stratigraphically higher on the Garvellachs, the origin of the carbonates (dètrital or newly precipitated) is unclear. Some ooids do occur above the base of the Port Askaig Formation on the Garvellachs, but could be reworked. Probable evaporite pseudomorphs also occur, signifying aridity, but not necessarily active evaporation.

Locality details

Unless you wish to circumnavigate the islands (see end of this section), you will approach Garbh Eilach from the east and be landed on the west side of a small bay (Fig. 9). The complete succession available in the Garvellachs can be viewed by a traverse along the east and south-east coast of Garbh Eilach. The localities are given from the base of the succession in this guide. This has the advantage of giving you warning of the approach of the boatman later in the day if the weather is deteriorating and you have to be taken off. Therefore walk along the coastline (cutting off the corner at the SE tip) to the base of the exposed succession.

Locality 1 (NM 676127) Islay Limestone (45 minutes). The Islay Limestone is exposed between here and locality 2 and consists dominantly of dolomitic mudrocks together with some limestone units in the lower half. Note the different orientations of bedding and cleavage to avoid subsequent confusion of these structures. The limestones display small stromatolite bioherms (see itinerary III for explanation of the origin of stromatolites) and some flake breccias. One unit with interlaminated dolomite and calcite has distinctive polygonal cracks of unknown origin. Poor preservation of textures in calcite suggests an aragonitic precursor for limestone.

At three horizons around 40m above the base of the exposed succession are bedding-plane exposures of radiating groups of tabular crystal pseudomorphs preserved in quartz and dolomite (Fig. 12a). The identity of the original crystals is uncertain. Nearby is a sandstone dyke (Fig. 12b).

The succession clearly represents shallow-water carbonates, but generally lacks structures or fabrics to allow closer interpretation, unlike the equivalent beds on Islay (Itinerary II).

Locality 2 (NM 677126 to 677124) Lower part of Port Askaig Formation (1 hour). The sharp base of well-cleaved dolomitic diamictite 1 is clearly exposed. There are three thin beds of coarser debris 1m below which could represent the first evidence of glacial activity. At one point, just underneath diamicitite 1 and exposed laterally over 5m distance, are recumbent folds which may be interpreted as glaciotectonic or slump folds (as in Fig. 10).

Figure 12. Itinerary I.

(a). Locality 2. Crystal pseudomorphs in dolostone of the Islay Limestone.

(b). Locality 2. Sandstone dyke penetrating Islay Limestone.

(c). Localities 9 and 10. Rhythmites above diamictite 32, folded by compaction around sandstone wedge.

(d). Locality 12. Diamictite bed no. 35.

(e). Locality 12. Triangular junction of sandstone wedges penetrating diamictite bed no. 35.

(f) Locality 12. Lag conglomerate above diamictite bed no. 35.

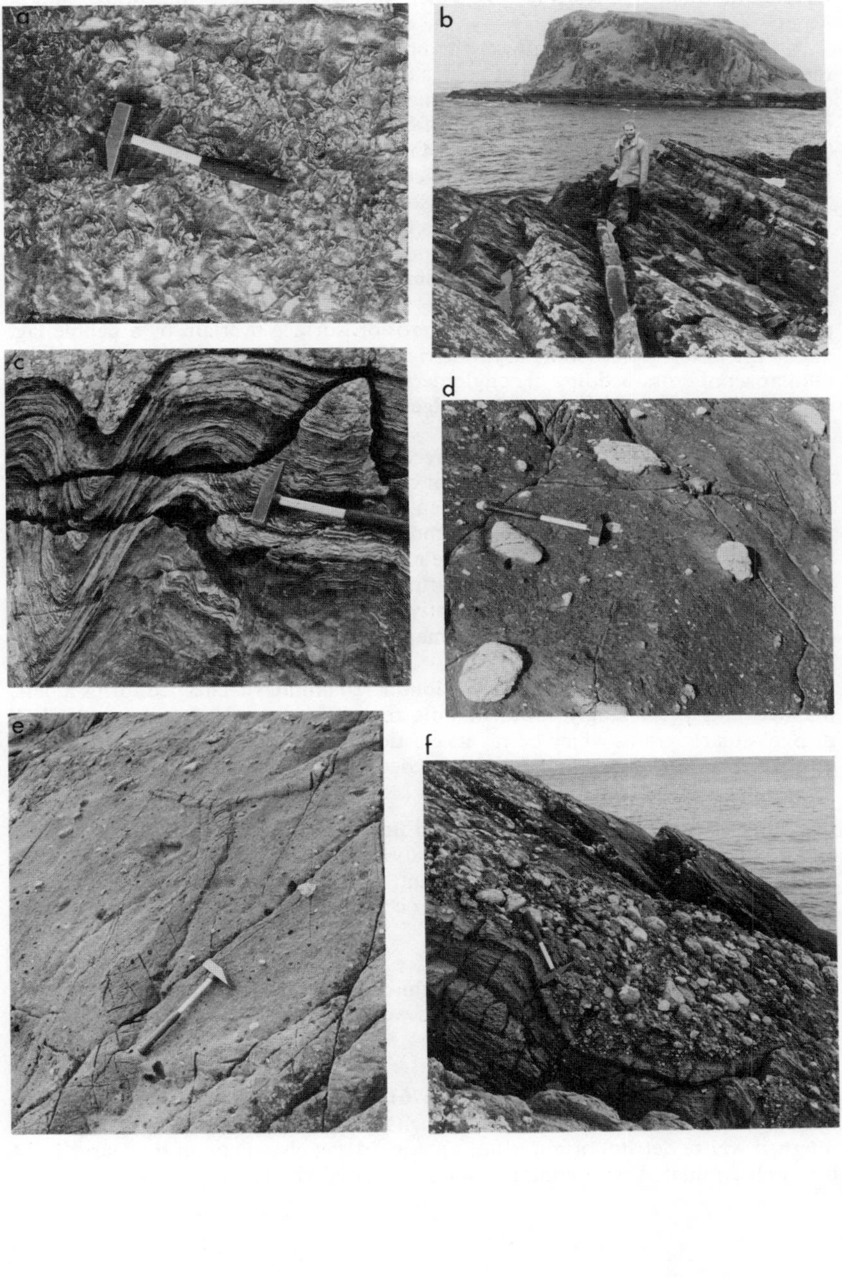
a
b
c
d
e
f

The interbed between diamicitites 1 and 2 appears similar to upper parts of the Islay Limestone; it has an erosive base; wave ripples occur indicating shallow water.

A few hundred metres away on the north coast of the island, diamictite 1 is represented by a few thin beds of coarse debris and is overlain by mudrocks with channelled sandstones (with ooids) and conglomerates (?tidal channels) and crystal pseudomorphs. 'Ovid masses' of Spencer (1971a) 1.5m beneath diamictite 1 are boudinaged, not stromatolitic. Marked lateral changes are also found on Dun Chonnuill where the base of diamictite 2 varies from erosive to gradational.

Moving towards locality 3, one passes over several dolomitic diamictites in which bedding can be searched for. It is easy to lose track of which diamictite is which, but diamictite 7 forms a prominent ridge running from the cliffline to Low Water Mark (Fig. 9). Interbeds are dolomitic sandstones and conglomerates with parallel lamination and cross-bedding. Interbed 9/8 as seen on the cliff is a particularly fine example with a basal erosion surface overlain by a pebble lag, abundant wave ripples (some asymmetrical to the NW) and a prominent graded tabular set of cross-bedding in conglomerate. Diamictite 9 has internal lamination and is followed by thick massive amalgamated diamicitites.

Locality 3 (NM 677 124) The Great Breccia (30 minutes). The base of the Great Breccia occurs at the top of a prominent cliff overlying a 3m conglomerate, sandy at its top. The Great Breccia is not seen at its best on this traverse, but even so the impure dolomitic matrix, common presence of limestone clasts and occurrence of some large blocks can be noted. One block of dolostone is at least 10m thick and vertically-dipping; another of limestone with dolomite laminae is around 10 by 3m and dips slightly steeper than regional bedding. The conglomerate at the top has a dark (magnetitic) matrix.

Locality 4 (NM 677123) The Lower Dolomite (20 minutes). This bed forms a pale, massive and perplexingly uniform dolostone. The same horizon on A'Chuli displays quartz grains which betray its clastic nature in the field, but here this can only be seen in thin section. It is succeeded by a dolostone conglomerate.

Locality 5 (NM 67701225) the 'Disrupted Beds' (20 minutes). These are a diverse and unique succession of sandstones, sandy dolostones, dolostone conglomerates and laminated magnetitic sandstones and pelites. Dropstones and apparently sedimentary boudinaged dolostone beds occur. Clearer exposures of this unit are found at locality 13.

Locality 6 (NM 67651220) Top of diamictite 15 (20 minutes). This forms a prominent bedding plane with clear sand wedges. The diamictite has few pebbles at the top and is highly dolomitic.

Localities 7 (NM 67651215) and 8 (NM 676121) Diamictites 17 to 26 (45 minutes). Sandy diamictite 17 has sand wedges at its top and is followed by a dolostone interbed whose detrital origin is not apparent here; elsewhere on the Garvellachs it is well laminated with common wave-generated ripples.

The succeeding diamictites contain a higher proportion of igneous clasts than hitherto. Diamictites 19, 23 and 25 have much internal bedding and were recognized as deposited from floating ice by Spencer (1971a). The tops of 22 and 26 (the latter is *locality 8*) contain sandstone wedges and load structures which Eyles and Eyles (1983) link genetically. Diamictite 26 is also overlain by a conglomerate lag.

Localities 9 (NM 67551195) and 10 (NM 675119) Higher Interbeds (45 minutes). Here are bedded sediments between diamictite 30 and the quartzite below diamictite 33, including two thin diamictites. The lower part includes dolostones and dolomitic siltstones with one prominently loaded or slumped horizon beneath a sandstone. Slightly higher are several metres of wave-ripple laminated sandstones. At *locality 10* massive quartzite passes up into laminated quartzite, then into rhythmically-laminated graded units with some dropstones. The rhythmites (varves) are highly dolomitic near the top, but this dolomite is secondary. The sediments are deeply penetrated by sandstone wedges adjacent to which the lamination is distorted by differential compaction during burial (Fig. 12c). The overlying quartzite is seen on the other side of the island to have cross-sets several metres high, comparable with the tidal shelf sandstones of the Jura Quartzite (Anderton, 1976). Now strike SW inland to cut off the tip of the island.

Locality 11 (NM 673118) Start of strike-parallel section (30 minutes to locality 12). The coastline now nearly follows the strike of the bedding. Here sandstone overlies diamictite 34.

Locality 12 (NM 66951175) Sandstone Wedges (30 minutes). Here diamictite 35 crops out (Fig. 12d); it has a variably dolomitic matrix. Prominent sandstone wedges occur (Fig. 12e), which appear to be true cross-cutting structures, not the discontinuous outcrops of a gently warped bed as Eyles & Clark (1985) have illustrated from this locality. A lag conglomerate caps the bed (Fig. 12f).

Although diamictites 35 to 38 crop out near the landing stage, remaining time would be more profitably spent visiting locality 13 by traversing the island to the NNW from near the cottage (15 minutes).

Locality 13 (NM 666122) Cliff of Disrupted Beds (30 minutes). Bealach nan Tarabairt. The high cliffs here have excellent exposures in the Disrupted Beds that provide a fitting climax to the day's geology. Attractive wave-washed pebbles from this unit occur in the cove below.

Highlights elsewhere on the islands:

The memoir of Spencer (1971a) is indispensable for anything beyond the day's traverse detailed above. The location of the other islands is shown in Fig. 9A.

Garbh Eilach: Top of diamictite 26, NW Garbh Eilach (NW 660127) where differing interpretations of relationships of dykes and loaded sandstone are given by Spencer (1971a) and Eyles & Clark (1985); large-scale cross-bedding below diamictite 33 (NW 660125) is visible from sea.

Eileach an Naoimh: the sea view of the enormous folded raft (known to the boatman as 'The Bubble') in the Great Breccia (Plate 1 in Spencer, 1971a, NM 639099) could be taken in as part of a circumnavigation of the islands prior to or after visiting the localities listed above. If landing on the island, the remains of St. Columba's monastery and beehive cells are well worth visiting (NM 640097). The best polygonal sand wedges are to be found at the top of diamictite 22 near its southern extremity of outcrop (Plate 8, Spencer, 1971a; Eyles & Clark, 1985; NM 646101). The most outstanding general section is to be found NE of the lighthouse on the shore and a NW-SE-trending raised beach cliff near the SW end of the island (NM 635094) from the Great Breccia through to diamictite 19. Another highlight is the lateral facies change at the base of diamictite 9 on the NE tip of the island (NM 646106).

A'Chuli: lateral changes (Spencer 1971a, Plate 11), including dramatic thinning from NE to SW (NM 658115 to NM 656114) in the Disrupted Beds.

Dun Chonnuill: lateral changes in the basal two diamictites (from NM 680128 to NM 682129).

ITINERARY II

Topmost Islay Limestone (Appin Group), Port Askaig and Bonahaven Formations (Argyll Group) Port Askaig area, Islay

I. J. FAIRCHILD

Maps: Ordnance Survey 1:50,000 sheet 60.
Geological: Plate 9 in Spencer (1971a).

Frequent car ferries to Islay depart from Kennacraig on West Loch Tarbert: to Port Ellen in the south of the island, and Port Askaig in the north-east. Details from Caledonian MacBrayne Ltd., The Ferry Terminal, Gourock PA19 1QP.

The first part of this itinerary (locality 1) demonstrates the character of the basal part of the Port Askaig Tillite and the top of the underlying Islay Limestone together with less detailed suggestions for other localities in the Port Askaig Formation. Here we are in the region of the type locality; exposures are good, although do not match the outstanding outcrops of the Garvellachs (Itinerary I).

The second and third localities are coastal exposures of the overlying Bonahaven Formation. Locality 2 is one of the finest and least deformed examples of a Dalradian sedimentary section. Locality 3 is the type section of the Bonahaven Formation.

Locality 1 (NR 415648). Strata around the base of the Port Askaig Tillite Formation, Beannan Buidhe, south of Lossit Farm (Figs. 13 and 14). Allow two to three hours.

It is necessary to contact the Manager, Dunlossit Estate, Ballygrant, Islay (Tel: Port Askaig 232) for permission if taking a party or during the deerstalking season (August to February).

Pending revision of Appin Group stratigraphy, the strata immediately underneath the Port Askaig Formation are referred to here as 'Islay Limestone' although belonging to a distinct stratigraphic unit above the dark limestones that typify the Appin Group carbonates. Evidently regression from an offshore to a coastal environment had occured some time prior to the onset of glacial sedimentation. Hence this regression is not obviously connected to a sea-level fall linked to ice-sheet formation, and there is no sign of temperate water facies, although these could have been removed by erosion. The sedimentology of the Port Askaig Tillite is discussed in the introduction to Itinerary I and in Figures 10 and 11.

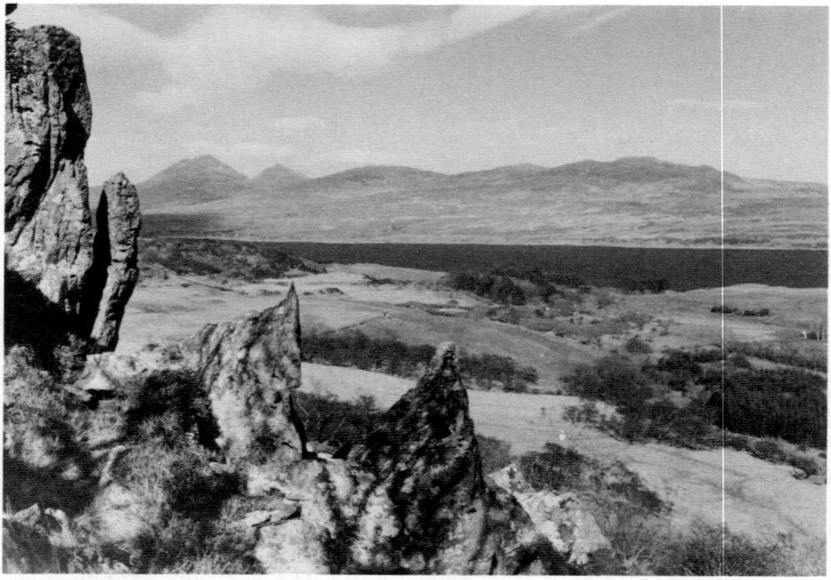

Figure 13. Diamictites in the Port Askaig Tillite Formation at Beannan Buidhe (locality 1, Itinerary II) with the island of Jura in the background.

Leave vehicles on the roadside at NR 409657 (Fig. 14) on the road to Lossit Farm. Walk up to the farm and continue east on the track until reaching the brow of the hill, then cross a gate to the south and walk along the edge of two fields NE of Beannan Dubh (Fig. 14). Having climbed the wall, continue southwards on the east side of the hill next to the fence and branch off to the right along flat ground at a point where the fence starts running steeply downhill.

1a. The cliff-line shows a massive diamictite (uppermost one in Figure 14) with dolostone clasts, overlying a quartzite at the cliffbase.

1b. The cliffline below and to the east displays a section from the top of the Disrupted Beds down to several metres below the top of the Islay Limestone (Fig. 14), including particularly good exposures of the erosive contact between fissured pale yellow dolostone at the top of the Islay Limestone and the overlying dolomitic sandstones (locally diamictite) referred to as the equivalent of the 'Great Breccia' of the Garvellachs by Spencer (1971a).

Above this cliff is a low crag on the flat ground at *1b* exhibiting a dolostone draped by a pale grey sandy diamictite. Probably all such dolostones within the Port Askaig Tillite are clastic accumulations of dolomite: this one can clearly be seen to be conglomeratic.

1c. Small exposures at the top of the slope and across a fault from *1b* are distinctive creamy-weathering intraclastic dolostones about 4m below the top of the Islay Limestone. The intraclasts have complex internal structures, features

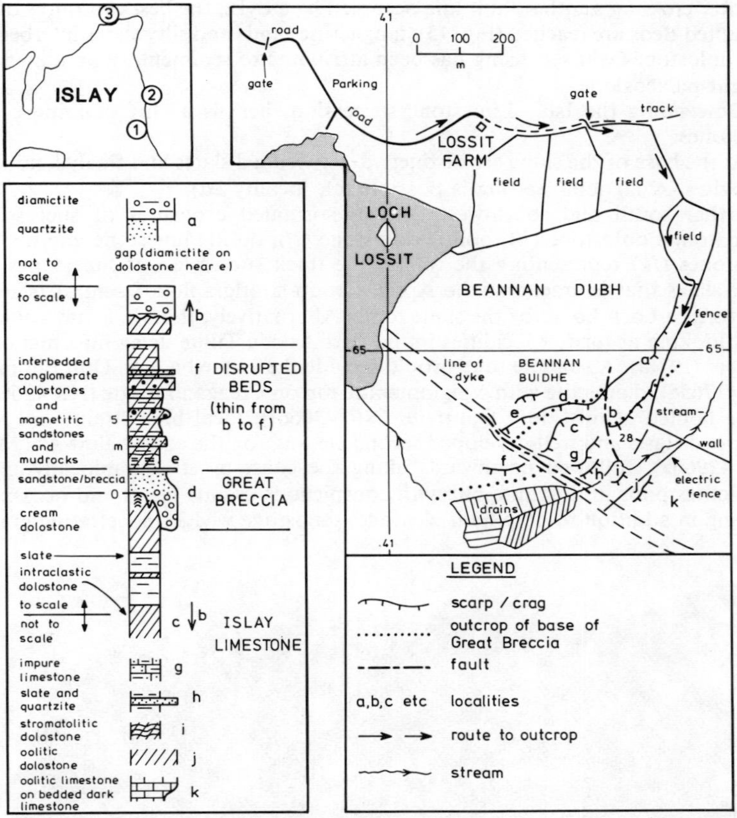

Figure 14. Itinerary II. Inset shows the whereabouts on northern Islay of localities 1 to 3. Location map and stratigraphic section across the Islay Limestone-Port Askaig Tillite boundary at locality 1, Beannan Buidhe. The base of the Port Askaig Tillite Formation is the base of the Great Breccia. The bedding dips uniformly northwest in the area of locations a to k.

referred to as catagraphs by Soviet workers who have attempted to use them for biostratigraphic purposes. They are probably stromatolite fragments.

1d. Further good exposures of the sandy Great Breccia, and underlying dolomite, locally seen to be stromatolitic. The Great Breccia is clearly quite different in character from that on the Garvellachs and is likely to represent shallow marine sands on a subaerial erosion surface (Fig. 11).

1e. In two locations, repeated by minor faults, is exposed a distinctive finely-laminated siltstone with dolostone pebbles, some of which are definitely dropstones. In the crag 25m north is exposed a diamictite draping a dolostone apparently not represented further east.

1f. After crossing another fault line occupied by a dyke, the best exposures of the Disrupted Beds are reached (Fig. 15): magnetitic sands and silty slates interbedded with dolostones whose lensing has been attributed to sedimentary boudinage on a slight palaeoslope.

1g. Descending the Islay Limestone succession, here is a cliff of impure pale limestones.

1h. At the base of the slope are distinctive interbedded slates and finely laminated quartzites. A lagoonal setting is possible (cf. locality 2d).

Further south and south-west there are isolated exposures of successively stromatolitic dolostone (*1i*), oolitic dolostone (*1j*), oolitic limestone and massive limestones (*1k*) representing the top of the thick succession of limestones and black slates that characterize the Appin Group stratigraphy of central Islay.

Return to Loch Lossit by the same route. Alternatively, the whole day could be spent looking at further localities in the Port Askaig Tillite using information in Spencer (1971a). A suitable route would include the Tillite base on Dun Bhoraraic (NR 417658); diamictite with conglomeratic top on Creagan Loisgte (NR 426663); Tillite faulted against Jura Quartzite (NR 430661); local high strain zone with deformed clasts and well-developed second cleavage on the coast below Am Meall (NR 429665), followed northwards along the coast by stratigraphically-higher diamictites poor in dolomite but with conspicuous granite clasts and occasional bedding in addition to dominant cleavage; sandstone wedges penetrating granite

Figure 15. Itinerary II, locality 1f: the Disrupted Beds.

conglomerate (NR 431676, on the coast just south of the wall which bounds the outlet stream from Loch Allan); varvites (lithified varves) along west side of Loch Allan (NR 425675, but overgrown in summer); returning SW along the estate road to Loch Lossit. Stratigraphically higher diamictites are well exposed on the shore between Port Askaig (NR 431692) and Caol Ila (NR 430699, i.e. immediately south of locality 2), but sedimentary structures are rare.

The sequence from massively-bedded Islay Limestone up through oolitic and stromatolitic carbonates to slate and quartzite interbedded with intraclastic and conglomeratic dolostones is well seen east of Keills from NR 422689 to NR 419696. The base of the Tillite is poorly exposed and complicated by minor faulting in this area.

Locality 2 (NR 430700) Uppermost Port Askaig Formation and lower part of Bonahaven Formation, Caol Ila. Table 6 summarizes the internal stratigraphy of the Bonahaven Formation. Allow two to three hours for this locality (this is flexible as the walking distance is short).

Drive to Caol Ila village and park just south of the distillery (NR 430699, Fig. 16A).

2a. The road cutting down to the distillery is stratigraphically about 300m below the top of the Port Askaig Tillite Formation. There are about 15m of slightly feldspathic quartzites (presumably an interbed between diamictites), mostly parallel-laminated, but with some current ripples and clay drapes: overall deposited in an energetic subtidal environment.

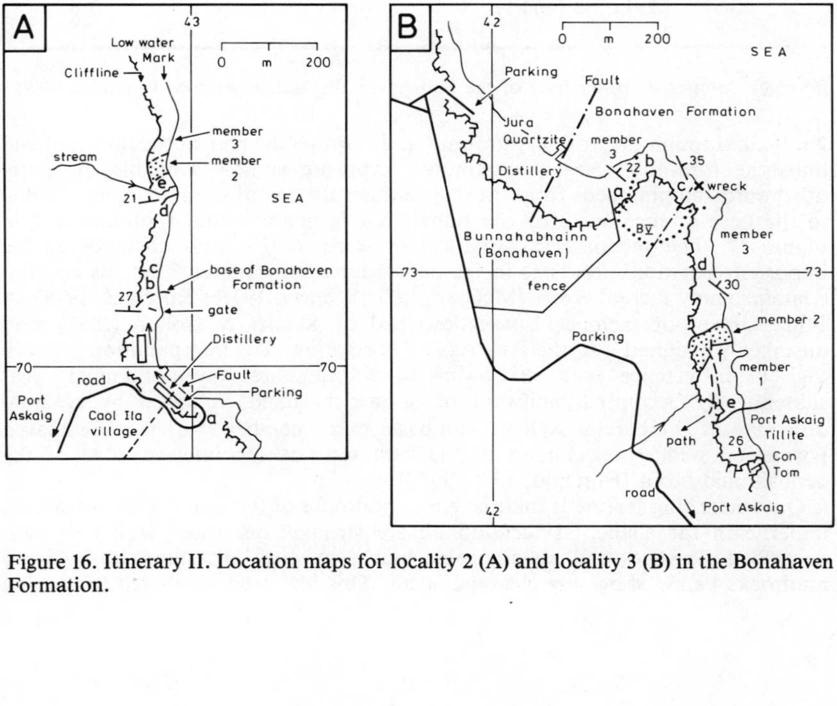

Figure 16. Itinerary II. Location maps for locality 2 (A) and locality 3 (B) in the Bonahaven Formation.

MEMBER	LITHOLOGY	THICKNESS (m)
4	Upper slate/heterolithic unit	20-25
	Central cream dolostone unit	0-12
	Lower sandstone/slate unit	20-25
3	Dolostones with thin graded sands; dolomitic sandstones; stromatolitic dolostones	0-200
2	Quartzite	22-30
1	Dolostones (unit 5)	0-10
	Sand/silt/mudstones (unit 4)	0-15
	Sandstones (unit 3)	0-11
	Flaser-bedded sandstones (unit 2)	0-18
	Mudrocks (unit 1)	0-8

Table 6. Composite stratigraphy of the Bonahaven Formation (see also Fairchild, 1989).

2b. Walk through the distillery grounds and through the gate at the northern end onto the foreshore. Nearly continuous exposure is now available in gently northwards-dipping beds from the quartzites at the top of the Port Askaig Tillite to the base of member 3 of the Bonahaven Formation and is summarized in Figure 17. The section was discussed by Klein (1970) who documented the importance of tidal processes in the depositional environment, but his account contains many factual errors (McCave, 1971; Spencer, 1971b; Fairchild, 1978). A 14m segment of member 1 was described by Kessler & Gollop (1988) who mistakenly assigned it to the Port Askaig Formation. The interpretation given in Fig. 17 in essence is a shallowing in a nearshore wave-dominated area, subsequently becoming landward of a barrier island, followed by eventual drowning of the barrier system. The basal part (member 1) of the Bonahaven Formation wedges out inland to the west towards the inferred edge of the depositional basin (Fairchild, 1978, 1979).

One interesting feature is that the basal mudrocks of the Bonahaven Formation underneath the shelter at location *2b* are strongly deformed with two well-developed cleavages and metamorphic biotite, whereas stratigraphically-higher mudrocks barely show any cleavage at all. This has been attributed to varying

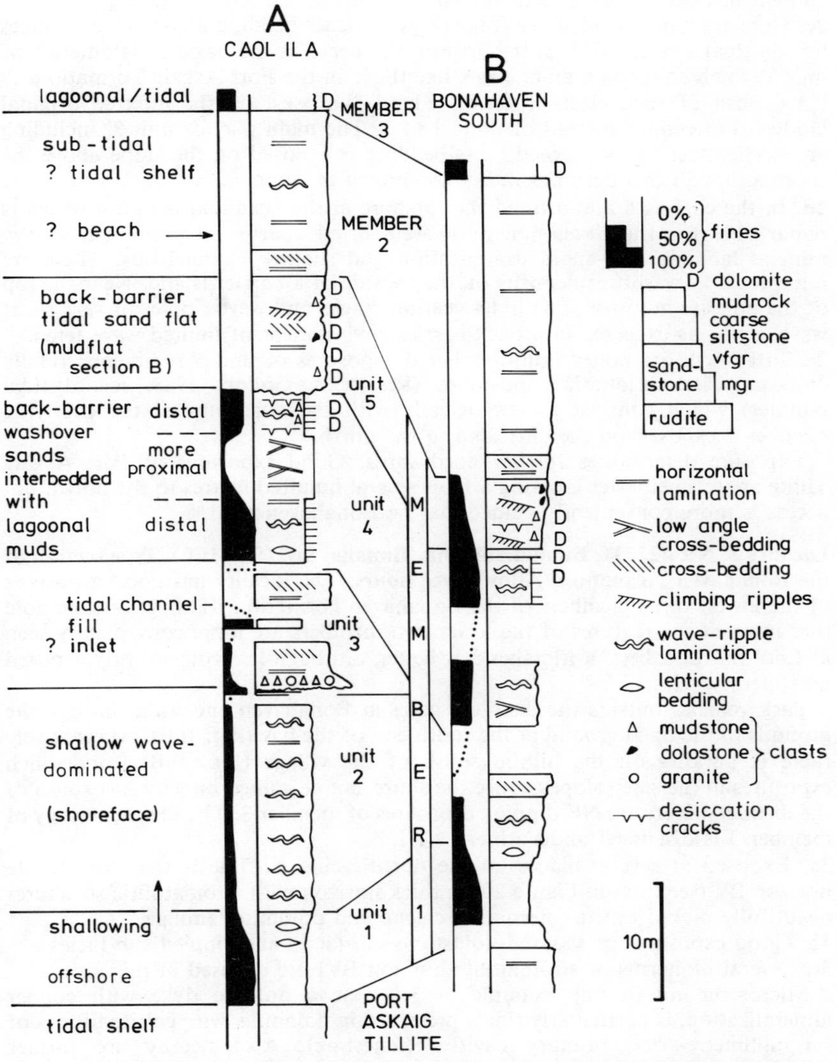

Figure 17. Itinerary II. Annotated log through sediments of the basal Bonahaven Formation (members 1 and 2) at locality 2, Caol Ila shore and locality 3, south of Bonahaven (referred to respectively as sections A and B by Spencer and Spencer, 1972).

fluid throughput during metamorphism (Fairchild, 1985b). A primary carbonate content has been lost by metamorphic reations in the biotite-bearing rocks.
2c. Here are unit 2 sandstones (Fig. 17) with flaser bedding and rippled surfaces (cf. de Raaf *et al.*, 1977). Just north on the beach is the basal conglomerate of unit 3 which contains granite clasts like those in the Port Askaig Formation. A lag deposit of such clasts is found inland 3km west (in the inferred original landward direction) instead of units 1 to 3. The main part of unit 3, including an excellent set of overturned cross-bedding is exposed on the slope above the shore although this becomes rather overgrown in summer.
2d. In the cliff at **d** and around the forshore at the headland is unit 4 which is remarkable for the development of well-sorted coarse siltstones with heavy mineral laminae, low-angle stratigication and shallow channel-fills. These are interpreted as washover deposits on the lee side of a barrier island. Near the top of the unit are mudstones with desiccation cracks and wave ripples of very short wavelength, as expected in a back-barrier environment of limited wave fetch.
2e. Just north are honeycomb-weathered exposures of unit 5 sediments: tidally cross-stratified dolomitic sandstones (Kessler & Gollop, 1988, record tidal bundles) which contrast mineralogically with the quartzites of the overlying member 2 exposed on the cliff 20m to the north.

Exposure deteriorates further northwards. Good exposures of Port Askaig Tillite are reached after crossing a fault several hundred metres to the north, but access is more conveniently gained via the Bonahaven road.

Locality 3 NR 422731, Bunnahabhainn (Bonahaven), (Fig. 16B). Type section of the Bonahaven Formation. Allow three hours. The locality has good exposures of the lowest three members of the Bonahaven Formation. If short of time note that most of the features of the lower two members are more conveniently seen at Caol Ila (Locality 2). Member 3 is better, although less conveniently exposed on itinerary III.

Park vehicles outside the distillery gates at Bonahaven and walk through the grounds to the open ground at the south end of the bay (Fig. 16B). Alternatively there is parking on the hilltop south of the village (Fig. 16B) from which exposures in the steep slopes above the shore can be gained directly just south of the distillery. Here are NE-dipping exposures of member 3. The sedimentology of member 3 is discussed under itinerary III.
3a. Exposed at several places on the north-facing cliffline is the stromatolite horizon BV (see inset in Figure 20), a thick horizon with stromatolitic structures beautifully picked out in alternating calcite and dolomite laminae.
3b. Good exposures of scoured dolostone sub-facies and rippled sub-facies.
3c. Several bioherms of stromatolite horizon BVI are exposed in this area.

Microstructure in one example at 3c, near a dolerite dyke with copper mineralization, is particularly finely preserved in dolomite, with calcite fillings of sub-millimetre-sized primary cavities (fenestrae). Also nearby are former anhydrite nodules up to several centimetres across, pseudomorphed by calcite with accessory quartz and pyrite.

Proceeding SE, horizon BV is passed again in a small cleft cut by the dyke previously mentioned just as the coastline swings to a N-S trend. Further south the exposure in member 3 is nearly continuous but more difficult of access.

3d. Here is a small E-W projecting ridge with calcitic stromatolites (horizon BIII) intermingled with cross-bedded oolites. Stromatolite horizon BIV and layered facies are also well exposed in the cliff above.

Now pass over remaining outcrops of the Bonahaven Formation so that member 1 can be traversed from its base as at locality 2.

3e. Units 1 and 2 are clearly exposed (Fig. 17), the former being much less deformed than at locality 2.

Exposure then deteriorate on the shore until near the top of unit 4.

3f. The main feature not seen at Caol Ila is the mud-dominance of unit 5 sediments which show evidence of both storm and tidal activity. Many of the sandstones here display quartz grains floating in dolomite probably representing calcareous soil profiles (dolocretes). Both early diagenetic and burial diagenetic dolomite are present with a complex growth history (Fairchild, 1980b). Orange-weathered dolomite has a replacive relationship to the black terrigenous mudstones although this is difficult to see in the field. Another fascinating laboratory discovery is that mudstones at the top of unit 5 contain abundant 0.1mm mica spheres which were interpreted by Fairchild (1977) as glauconitized microfossils. They are present in some mudclasts at Caol Ila and in mudstones inland, but only at this horizon. No comparable discoveries are known anywhere else.

The cliff may be scaled here by means of a steep path 200m north of Con Tom (Fig. 16B). Returning via the cliff top is more convenient than returning by the shore if vehicles were parked south of the village.

ITINERARY III

Bonahaven Formation (Argyll Group), North Coast of Islay

I. J. FAIRCHILD

Maps: Ordnance Survey 1:50,000 sheet 60.
Geological: Fairchild (1980c, figure 1)

This unspoilt coastline is several miles from the nearest road and is reached by walking across open moorland: total distance for the day is about 20km (Fig. 18). Allow a total of about 9½ hours. Both the Dalradian geology and the raised-beach scenery (Fig. 19B) are outstanding and well worth the walk. Access is normally unrestricted, but in August and September deerstalking will be in progress and you should contact the Factor, Islay Estates Company, Bridgend, Islay PA44 7PB (Tel: Bowmore 221) for permission.

Summary of sedimentology. The stratigraphic units seen are the Jura Quartzite and members 2, 3 and 4 of the underlying Bonahaven 'Dolomite' Formation. Member 2 is a quartzite as seen on itinerary II, locality 2e. Member 3 is the geological highlight and consists of dolomitic sediments which Fairchild (1980a) has divided into the following facies (Fig. 20):

(i) Stromatolites (see also Spencer & Spencer, 1972). These are continuous beds (biostromes) or localized occurrences (bioherms) of laminated dolostone, sometimes with complex growth structures (Fig. 20A). They formed from a mixture of sedimentation and carbonate precipitation within sticky microbial ('algal') mats, and are common in Precambrian carbonate rocks in the absence of competition from, and predation by, other organisms. Somewhat analogous structures form today in current-swept or hypersaline or intertidal environments in for example the Caribbean, Australia, and the Persian Gulf. Precambrian analogues were more widely distributed.

(ii) Sandstone facies (Fig. 20B). These are 0.1–3m thick beds of medium-grained dolomitic sandstone (sometimes oolitic) characteristically cross-bedded with sets 3–30cm thick. Palaeocurrents are often bidirectional in a given bed and nearly radial overall indicating an origin related to inshore tidal flows. Wave-rippled layers also occur. There are common desiccated (pure) dolostone beds and derived intraclasts.

(iii) Layered facies (Fig. 20C). These are units up to several metres thick consisting of cm-scale alternations of fine-grained dolomitic sandstones and variably dolomitic mudstones. The coarser layers were deposited by storms and the finer layers represent a combination of suspension sedimention, and dolomite precipitation. This facies is divided into three sub-facies.

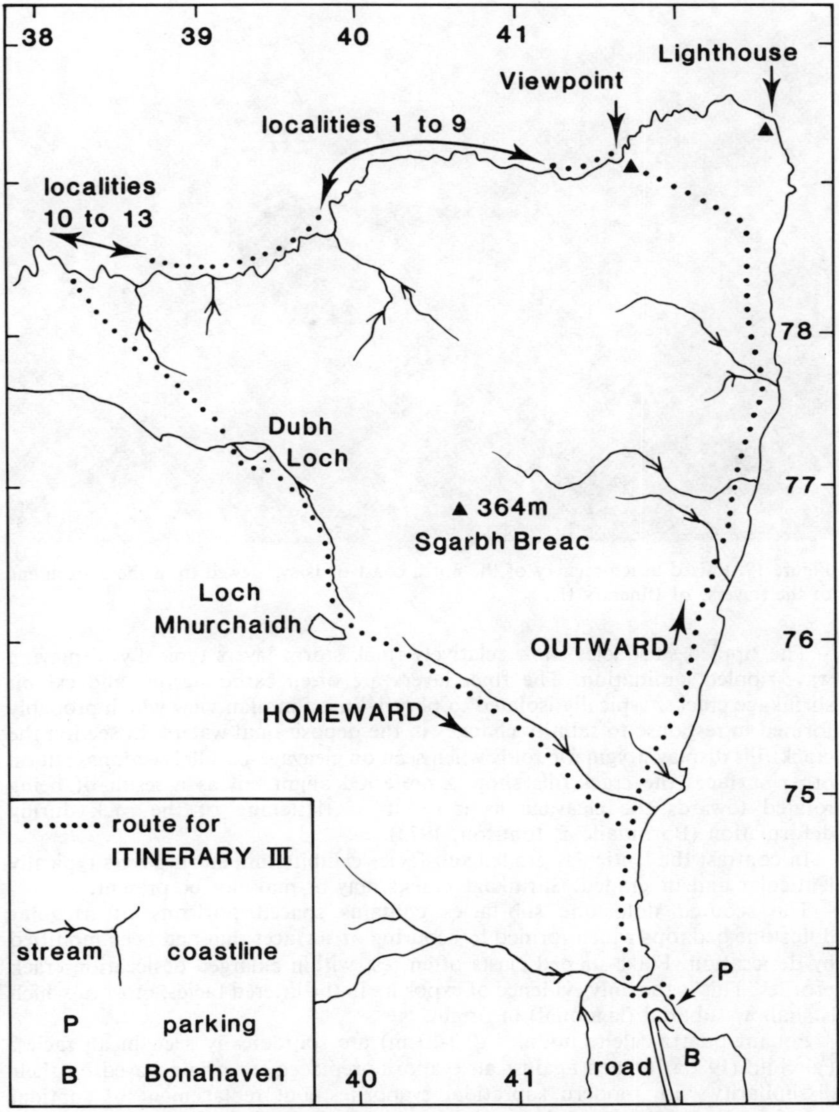

Figure 18. Map to illustrate walk to and from localities of Itinerary III.

Figure 19. Raised beach scenery of the north coast of Islay, viewed from the eastern end of the traverse of Itinerary III.

The rippled sub-facies show relatively thick storm layers typically displaying wave-rippled lamination. The finer layers are often carbonaceous and exhibit shrinkage cracks, typically isolated to poorly-linked in plan view which probably formed in response to salinity changes in the depositional waters. In section the crack-fills display ptygmatic folds when seen on cleavage-parallel sections, but on other surfaces the crack-fills show a preferred alignment as a result of being rotated towards the cleavage as a result of flattening of the rock during deformation (Borradaile & Johnson, 1973).

In contrast the lenticular-graded sub-facies exhibits thin storm layers typically lenticular and/or graded. Shrinkage cracks may or may not be present.

The scoured dolostone sub-facies contains spaced horizons of irregular dolostone bed tops which formed by scouring of surfaces that had been modified by desiccation. Flake-shaped clasts often rest within enlarged desiccation crack profiles. This is the only evidence of exposure in the layered facies, most of which is shallow subtidal (lagoonal) in origin.

Equant quartz-calcite nodules (0.3-10cm) are sporadically seen in all facies. Fairchild (1980a) argued against an evaporite-replacement origin based on their dissimilarity with modern supratidal evaporites, but replacement of subtidal anhydrite crystals and nodules now seems highly likely given that anhydrite relics are preserved in near-identical facies in East Greenland (Fairchild, 1989; Fairchild and Herrington, 1989).

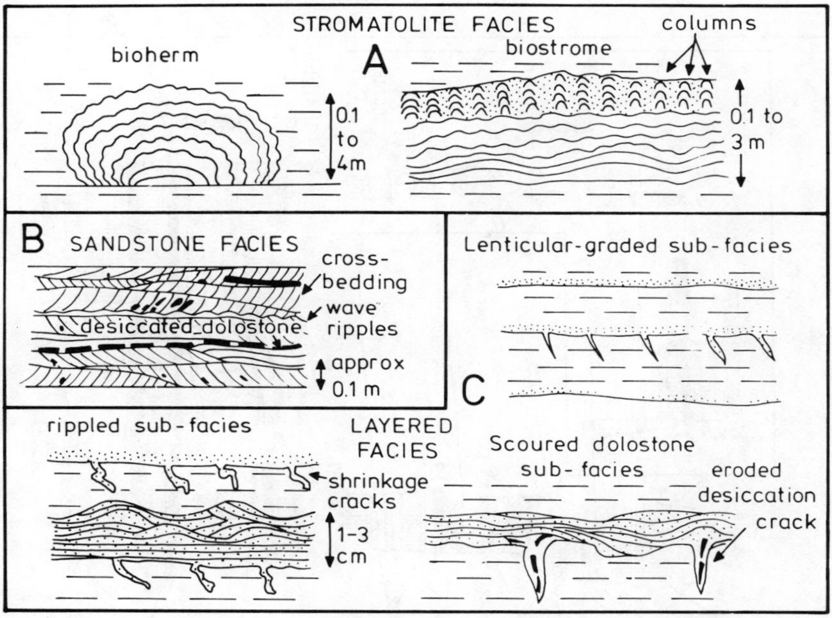

Figure 20. Itineraries II and III. Summary of the sedimentary facies in member 3 of the Bonahaven Formation.

Member 3 shows a random stacking of facies (Fig. 21) indicating a complex patchwork of exposed and subtidal areas, with localized tidal currents and expanses of microbial mats, all broadly lagoonal in origin. Analogous rocks from East Greenland exhibit a simple shallowing-upwards sequence which shows us that the lagoon could have passed directly offshore into a shoreface dominated by storm deposits. The storm events must have been infrequent, allowing a predominantly fine-grained sequence to accumulate against the shoreline.

Member 4 of the Bonahaven Formation consists mostly of rather deformed terrigenous sediments: fine sands and slates with a central unit, wedging out to the SE towards Bonahaven, of pure dolostone. The member is interpreted as a transgressive-regressive cycle with the dolotone representing a supratidal flat. The uppermost, muddy part of the member passes by interbedding into the tidal shelf sandstones (quartzites) of the Jura Quartzite (Anderton, 1976).

Route and locality details. Leave vehicles outside the gates to the distillery at Bonahaven (Bunnahabhainn, Fig. 16B, 18) and proceed north along the shore (or just seaward of the bungalow on the clifftop if the tide is high). Jura Quartzite crops out on the shore in typical highly jointed condition. Cross the stream by the bridge (NR 416735) and follow the path which is parallel both to the coast and a line of telegraph poles for about 5km to around NR 425782, when most of the Ruvaal lighthouse tower is visible. Now head NNW up to the col (NR 419788) west of Cnoc na Faire west of the lighthouse. Continue NW aiming for

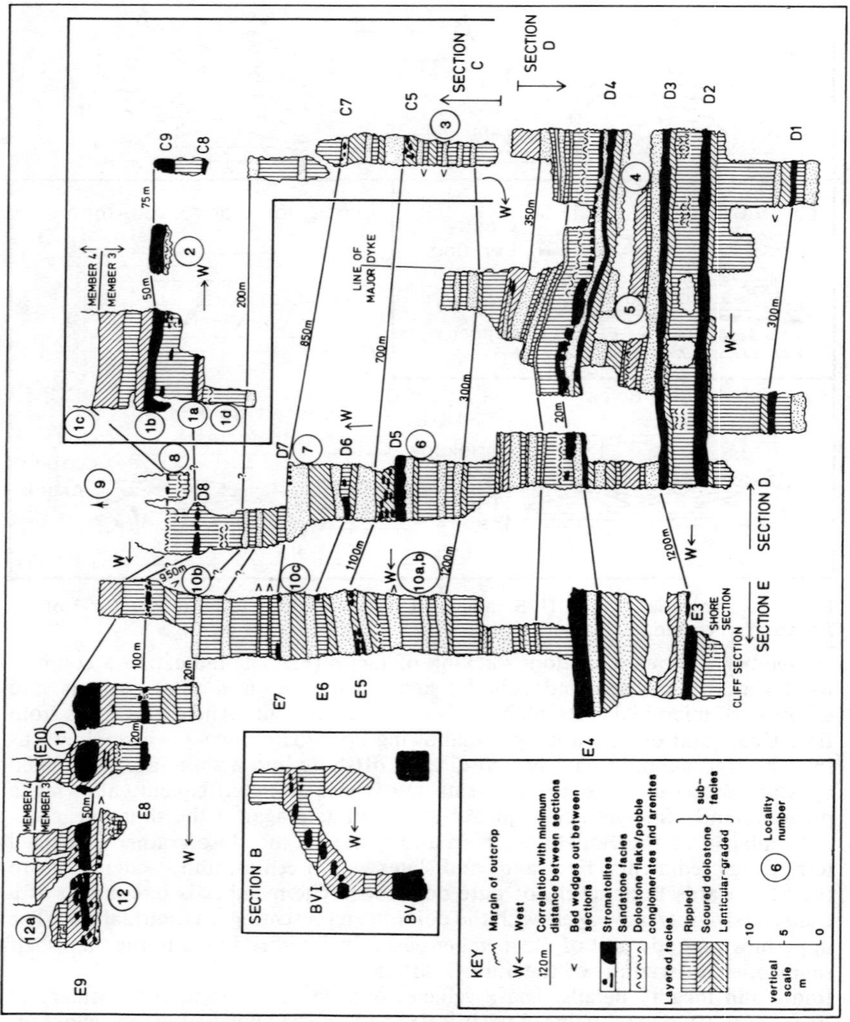

Figure 21. Itinerary III. Reconstruction of the geometry of the facies units of member 3 of the Bonahaven Formation, north coast of Islay, with position of localities. Note the stromatolite horizons are coded by the section letter followed by a number. The inset shows the facies geometry at the top of exposed member 3 at section B (locality 3, Itinerary II).

the sandy beach of Bagh an da Dhorius when it comes into view. There is a single steep path (NR 415787, Fig. 22) down the cliffs (the next one is 1km west) immediately beneath the telegraph pole that used to bear the telephone connection to Colonsay.

From the clifftop there is a good view of the famous raised beach terraces (Fig. 19, viewpoint indicated on Fig. 18) which post-date the last glacial maximum. The shoreline displays Dalradian geology cut by several upstanding Tertiary dolerite dykes. The following list of localities picks out highlights of the near continuous exposures. Since the outcrops are cut every few metres by minor faults (the most important of which are shown on Fig. 22) it is often difficult to follow individual beds more than a few metres or tens of metres, but the reconstructed facies geometry is shown in Figure 21. Note that it would be easy to miss the splendid geology at the end of the sections by spending too long on the earlier localities. It is suggested that given a period of about 6 hours on the exposures, no more than 2½ hours should be spent on the first 5 localities and 1½ hours on localities 6 to 9.

The member 4-Jura Quartzite junction is well exposed at the east end of the bay Bagh an da Dhorius, but is also seen later. Therefore proceed to the west side of the bay stopping near high-water mark at a small promontory.

Locality 1a Stromatolite bed C8 (Figs. 21, 23a) is well exposed overlying scoured dolostone sub-facies. It has well-shaped columnar growth forms in the sandy upper portion.

1b. Downfaulted to the shore just east is a thick mixed dolomitic-calcitic stromatolite (C9) with domal growth forms.

1c. Basal member 4 flaser-bedded sands and grey muds are clearly exposed 20m to the SE where they are contact-metamorphosed next to a Tertiary dyke.

1d. This low stack displays good layered facies with deformed shrinkage cracks. A thin storm horizon of dolostone breccia is present near the top, repeated by numerous minor faults. Most of the dolomite clasts have been replaced by burial diagenetic quartz-albite mosaics and resemble siltstone in the field (Fairchild, 1985b). Just east is a sandstone facies bed which, like most of the facies units (beds), can be correlated with section E, 2.5km to the west.

Locality 2 Here there is a locally thick development of stromatolitic flake breccia at the base of C9.

Locality 3 The clearest exposures here are on low outcrops just below high-water mark.

3a. good lenticular pyritic sand laminae in lenticular-graded subfacies lacking shrinkage cracks.

3b. rippled sub-facies with black carbonaceous dolomitic mudstones displaying shrinkage cracks (similar to locality 10a, Fig. 23b).

3c. Bedding plane exposures of isolate shrinkage cracks.

Locality 4 Between two prominent dykes are good exposures of the strata up to stromatolite horizon D4, although lowest beds are seaweed-covered, hence obscure. There are common wave-rippled bedding surfaces above and below D2

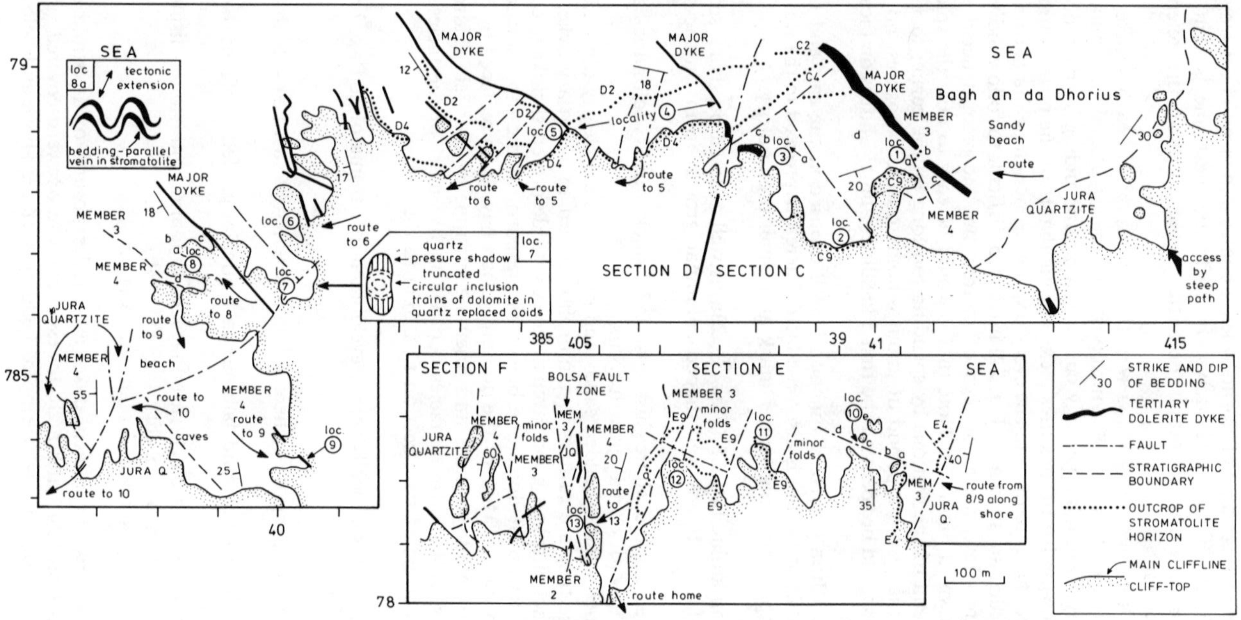

Figure 22. Itinerary III. Locality maps of the Bonahaven Formation (members 2 to 4) and Jura Quartzite, north coast of Islay (sections, C, D and E of Spencer and Spencer, 1972, and section F of Fairchild, 1980c). The cliffline is drawn from large-scale aerial photographs: superposition of the National Grid is approximate.

and flake breccia lenses and sections through wave-ripple lamination between D2 and D3. D2 and D3 are excellent examples of biostromal stromatolites with exhumed domes in places. D4 is a double stromatolite horizon separated by sandstone facies, and is biohermal in part (Fig. 21).

It is necessary, except at low spring tide, to climb the cliff to pass the next dyke, descending 100m west of the dyke.

Locality 5 Immediately west of the dyke on the main raised beach cliff is an excellent face in a sandstone facies bed (Fig. 23c). At the base of the bed is a preserved megaripple (or dune) in section, draped by a dolostone layer. Now ascend the raised beach platform and walk 400m west.

Locality 6 Descend a prominent bedding plane to shore level, just east of a ridge on the shore with prominent open folds, to view stromatolite horizon E5 which displays irregular stromatolite bioherms growing within sandstone facies. Locally, large dolostone clasts can be seen on foresets of cross-bedding.

Locality 7 On the west side of the bay, at the base of a cliff above the grassy platform, is an oolitic sandstone facies bed which displays remarkable pressure solution phenomena in thin section (see inset in Fig. 22 and Fairchild, 1985).

Again ascend the cliff, cross the line of a prominent dyke and descend to just above shore level.

Locality 8 The deformation history in a 200-300m-wide zone around this locality is subtly complex with the earliest cleavage (and associated rotated sandstone shrinkage-crack-fillings) having a northwest-southeast strike and being crenulated by a cleavage having the normal Caledonoid (northeast-southwest) trend which in turn is affected by a late crenulation cleavage dipping WNW (Fairchild, 1980c). The bedding is homoclinal throughout.

8a. The locally biohermal stromatolite D8 is clearly exposed with a columnar upper part terminated by a storm layer of fine sandstone. Bedding-parallel quartz-calcite veins, common in the stromatolites in the area, are here clearly only present on one-side of stromatolite domes (inset in Fig. 22) demonstrating their origin by extension during tectonic deformation.

8b. Good examples of tectonically-deformed sedimentary structures occur on a small vertical E-facing rock surface (Fig. 23d).

8c. Locality where all three cleavages can be seen (first cleavage dips 35-40° SW; second dips 30-35° ESE; third dips 45° WNW).

8d. Member 3-member 4 boundary, 100m SW of 8c. If there was a bedding-parallel fault at this boundary it might explain the local structural complications, as well as accounting for the truncated stratigraphy at the top of member 3 compared with sections C and E (Fig. 21), but no fault in this orientation is discernable.

Locality 9 A diversion to the back of a narrow gully to the south of the coastline allows study of a 2m-wide zone of contact metamorphism of the member 4 dolostone unit to a calcite-serpentine marble next to a Tertiary dyke.

a
b
c
d
e

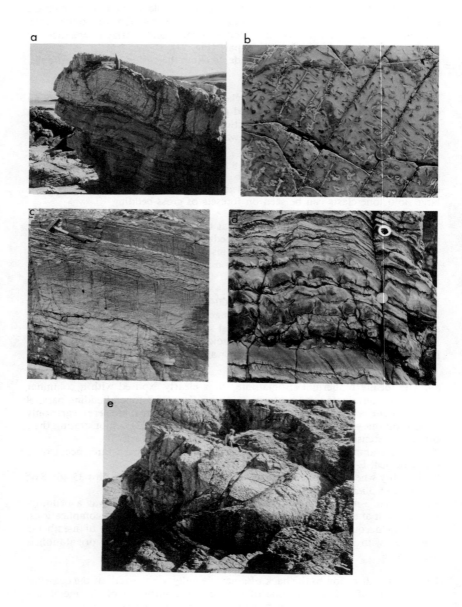

Now pass north of the caves in the raised beach cliff and ascend to the clifftop, descending immediately to the west, passing examples of large-scale cross-bedding in the Jura Quartzite. Continue along the shoreline for about 600m until a major NNE-SSW fault is crossed and member 3 exposures return.

Locality 10 Exposures north of a WNW-ESE fault line between cliff and small sea stacks on the shore.
10a. Numerous pebbles and good exposures in rock pools of rippled sub-facies (Fig 23b).
10b. Sandstone facies beds on small cliffs.
10c. Lenticular-graded sub-facies with mm-scale pseudomorphs after anhydrite on the south face of a sea stack opposite folds in the main cliff.
10d. Three metres above the cobbled shore are exposures of scour-enlarged deep desiccation cracks in scoured dolostone sub-facies.
10e. Best viewed from just west of 10d are striking exposures, on a prominent sea stack, of large-wavelength (50cm) wave ripples on the top of a sandstone facies bed. Now proceed further west passing over several prominent minor folds.

Locality 11 Where the foreshore is narrowest (and difficult to traverse around high spring tide) there is a spectacular exposure of a 4m-high stromatolite bioherm (horizon E9) in seawards-dipping beds (Fig. 23e). The bioherms have smooth, near vertical margins.

Locality 12 Around this promontory are a number of excellent exposures, especially just above high-water mark, cut by several faults and minor folds. Highlights include numerous exhumed stromatolite bioherms and, in overlying scoured dolostone sub-facies, arenites of dolostone fragments, load casts and desiccated and scoured dolostone surfaces, often capped by flake breccias.
12a. This is the only place where the flake-filled scours in the scoured dolostone sub-facies can be seen to be polygonal in plan demonstrating their origin as enlarged desiccation profiles.

Now walk across member 4 sediments and through a gap in the prominent cliff of massive member 4 dolostone.

Figure 23. Itinerary III.
(a). Locality 1a. Stromatolite bed C8.

(b). Locality 10a. Rippled sub-facies with sedimentary fills of shrinkage cracks aligned by tectonic deformation.

(c). Locality 5. Sandstone facies.

(d). Locality 8b. Deformed sedimentary structures in layered facies.

(e). Locality 11. Stromatolite bioherm. Bedding in surrounding strata dips uniformly towards lower right in photograph.

Locality 13 Here is the Bolsa fault zone. The fault can be traced inland for at least 12km, and is often parallel to near-vertical rocks, yet has a considerable stratigraphic displacement. Member 3 is always thinner west of the fault and is absent in the southern area west of the fault. Fairchild (1980c) suggested that there was ductile movement (sliding) along the fault during the main Caledonian deformation. It seems likely that it had a longer history and originated as one of the major syn-depositional listric faults that controlled Argyll Group Dalradian sedimentation (Anderton, 1985).

On the cliffline to the west can be observed a succession through from the top of member 2, a thin member 3 and a complete member 4 to the Jura Quartzite. On the shore the structure is extremely complex with intensely deformed and virtually undeformed strata juxtaposed, shear surfaces, zones of tight folding, folded faults and quartz veining.

The return to Bonahaven (Fig. 18) is best made by returning SE over the moorland which affords some fine views. Allow 1½ to 2 hours for the walk.

ITINERARY IV

Appin Group, Loch Leven District

J. E. TREAGUS

Maps: Geological Survey 1: 50,000 Sheet 53 Ben Nevis
Ordnance Survey 1:50,000 Tourist Map, Ben Nevis and Glen Coe or Sheets 41 and 49.

This excursion examines the lithostratigraphy of the Appin Group, Table 4) in the type area, and its junction with the Grampian Group.

The sedimentary environments of these rocks have been commented on by Hickman (1975) and Anderton (1985). The psammites of the 'young Moine' or Grampian Group are significantly more feldspathic than those of the Appin Group above and geochemical distinctions are strong. Estuarine or inter-tidal conditions have been suggested for these rocks. The Appin Group sediments are generally agreed to have been deposited on a shallow shelf, the sands deposited in tidal conditions and periods of subsidence represented by intervening muds. The black mud deposits with associated dark carbonaceous limestones probably represent deeper anoxic conditions.

This sequence and that seen on Islay (Itinerary II) should be compared with that described in the Schiehallion area (Itinerary V) where the equivalent formations can be seen in a much abbreviated state (Fig. 24). Discussion concerning the reasons for this contrast and the implications for the palaeogeography are found in the introduction to the Schiehallion area. Also shown on Fig. 24 are generalised thickness and facies changes within the Loch Leven area, which show rapid thinning westward of the quartzites in the lower Lochaber Subgroup, as well as the changes eastward, towards the Schiehallion area. The changes suggest that the central and eastern area of Loch Leven (locs. 7-11) was subject to rapid subsidence compared with the areas to the northwest and southeast. These changes are not explored in the excursion, but can readily be examined in the excellent outcrops around the loch or the hillside crags.

In order to understand the stratigraphic sequence in the Loch Leven area it is necessary to appreciate the fundamental structural geometry of the area. This is shown in the inset to Figure 25 (after Roberts and Treagus, 1977a) as the product of large-scale D_1 isoclinal folds which once faced to the northwest and were subsequently refolded by upright D_2 structures. Many outcrops described below are affected by minor folds of up to four generations and it is necessary to appreciate the geometry of these as well as that of the major folds when interpreting sedimentary structures, both from the point of view of the relative

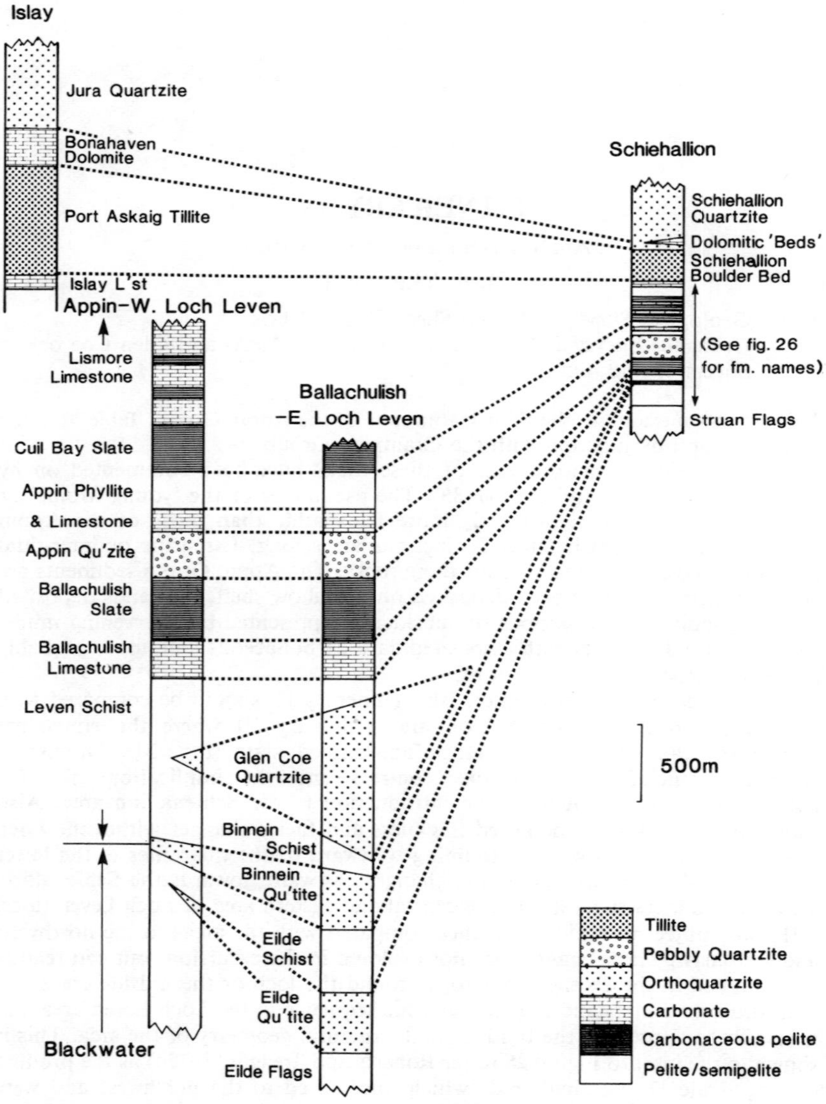

Figure 24. A comparison of thicknesses of formations in the Loch Leven (and Islay) area with those at Schiehallion.

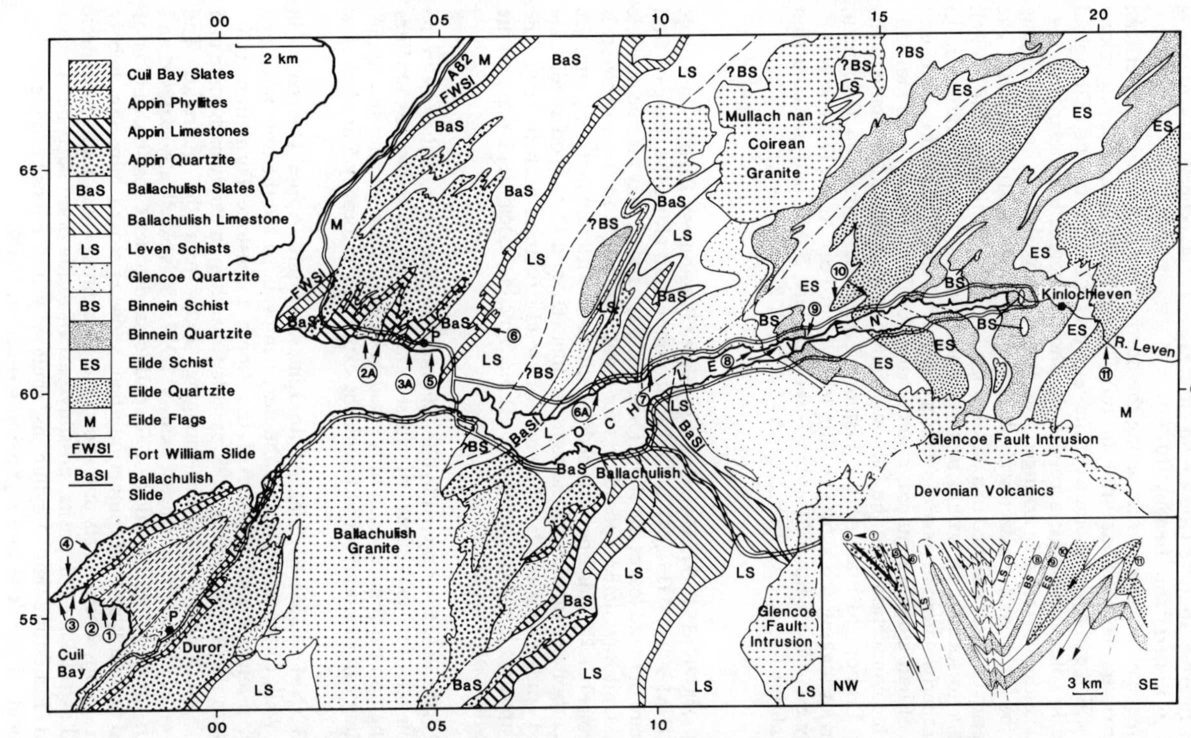

Figure 25. Map of Loch Leven area for Itinerary IV. P indicates principal car-parking locations. Inset shows schematic profile of D_1 (heavy lines with arrow heads for facing) and D_2 folds (dashed lines) and approximate level of localities. (After Roberts and Treagus, 1977a, Figs. 1 and 2).

age of formations and of palaeogeographic reconstruction. Full details of the structural interpretation can be found in Treagus (1974) Roberts (1976) and a summary in Roberts and Treagus (1977a).

An infrequent bus service runs along the north shore of Loch Leven between Kinlochleven and Fort William (rail station) There are several large lay-bys along this road which can accommodate coaches and cars. Low tide can be of marginal advantage in some exposures; access to the shore is generally unrestricted.

The localities (1-11) are arranged, as far as possible, in a descending stratigraphic order and consecutively below those of Islay (Itinerary II). The excursion can be accomplished in a day, but the hillside localities 6 and 10, as well as the walk to locality 11, would best be omitted if the other localities are to studied properly. Alternatives are given for localities 2 and 3, if a more condensed excursion of half a day is required, also omitting localities 1 and 11. To make the stratigraphic connection with the Islay succession, a visit should be made to the Island of Lismore to examine the Lismore Limestone Formation (Hickman, 1975). Ferries making the short crossing leave from Port Appin (NM 904455).

Full day excursion : either localities 1-10 or 2A, 3A, 5 - 11; half-day excursion either localities 1-4, 5, 6A, 7 or 2A, 3A, 5, 6A, 7, 8.

Locality 1 (NM 976554 - 973554). Cuil Bay Slate (30 minutes). Park in the village of Duror (NM 990549) (Fig.24) and take the minor road along the shore of Cuil Bay to where the road leaves the shore (NM 978553, parking may also be possible here). The Cuil Bay Slate, exposed on four small peninsulas to the northwest, is a pyritiferous black mudstone with beds of siltstone, with rare beds of psammite and grey carbonate. In spite of the tight folding (D_1 and D_2), good small scale silt-to-mud graded beds can be observed with load structures at their bases. The beds face upwards in the core of the D_1 Appin Syncline. Localities 2-4 are on the northwest limb of this fold.

Locality 2 (NM 969555) Appin Phyllite (20 minutes). Walk across the bay to the next peninsula for exposures of these chlorite-muscovite-biotite phyllites representing non-carbonaceous muddy siltstones. Small-scale grading and ripple-drift bedding can be observed, although the exposures at locality 5 are superior.

Locality 3 (NM 963556-967558) Appin Limestone and Appin Quartzite (45 minutes). Walk to the southwest of the next peninsula to see the dolomite, grey carbonate, psammite and phyllite of the Appin Limestone Formation at its junction with the Appin Quartzite. Ripple-drift bedding in sandy carbonate and psammite demonstrates southeast-younging away from the quartzite. The quartzite, especially to the northeast near NM 967558, is excellently exposed and shows beds up to 0.5 metre thick of felspathic sandstone. Cross-bedding is of trough and tabular type with thinner interbeds showing cross-lamination. Pebbly beds often occupy bottom sets and show crude grading. These rocks have been interpreted as tidal shelf deposits, possibly part of a tide-dominated delta, with the Appin Limestone and Phyllite as shallow water deposits representing abandonment of the delta and regression (Anderton 1985).

Locality 4 (NM 964559-971565). Transition to Ballachulish Slate (30 minutes). The lower part of the Appin Quartzite is a distinctive striped transition to the Ballachulish Slate. Beds of fine quartzite within black pyritiferous slate exhibit a great variety of sedimentary structures including slump folds and breccias, grading, load-structures, dykelets and cross-bedding. Younging is to the southeast. 30 minutes.

If return from this exposure is made by crossing to the farm-track at NN 978560, exposures transitional from the Appin Phyllite to Cuil Bay Slate may be examined near this point.

Locality 5 (NN 049611) Ballachulish Slate (20 minutes). From Duror drive 12 km north on the A828 turning towards Fort William after crossing the Ballachulish Bridge. Park west of a petrol station on the south side of the road. The quarry to the north of the road is in Ballachulish Slate, but now on the east limb of the Appin Syncline. The black pyritiferous slates (here pyrrhotitic, due to contact metamorphism) contain silty and psammitic beds with small-scale graded bedding younging NW. These dark muds, like those represented by the Cuil Bay Slate of loc. 1, imply deposition in relatively deep deoxygenated water, although Hall (1982) interprets the quartz-dolomite-pyrrhotite laths as pseudomorphs after gypsum, indicating evaporative conditions. 20 minutes.

In addition, or as alternative to localities 3 and 2, the Appin Quartzite-Limestone-Phyllite succession may be examined from this locality (1 hour). The Appin Quartzite is excellently exposed on the shore at NN 043610 (loc 3A) with trough cross-bedding younging NW. The Appin Limestone and Phyllite are well exposed to the west, especially in the core of the syncline between NN 036613 and 033613 (loc 2A). (One hour).

Locality 6 (NN 060617-061602) Ballachulish Limestone – Leven Schist) (1½ hours). If the visitor wishes to see the Ballachulish Limestone and upper Leven Schist which intervene between the Ballachulish Slate and the Leven Schist of locality 7, he should climb the hill at NN 060617 from locality 5. Here the 'Limestone' comprises a graphitic carbonate at its top, gradational to the Ballachulish Slate, calcareous schist in its centre and creamy dolomite with schist intercalations at its junction with the Leven Schist. Particularly good exposures of the upper Leven Schist can be examined on the return around NN 061602, above and to the north of the road. These rather homogeneous muscovite-biotite-chlorite phyllites contain silty and occasionally sandy ribs which exhibit small-scale grading and cross-lamination. One and a half hours.

Alternatively, an exposure of the 'limestone' can be quickly visited, en route to locality 7, at NN 084600 on the loch shore (loc. 6A, 20 minutes).

The association of non-carbonaceous muds, silts and carbonate is indicative of a clear open basin.

Localities 7-9 enable the visitor to examine the sequence of three pelites and three quartzites, comprising the Lochaber Subgroup at the base of the Appin Group. These exposures are of historic interest in that they were amongst the first in Highland geology where sedimentary structures were used to establish a stratigraphic sequence, which in turn allowed the complexities of the major structure to be resolved (Bailey 1930). Some of this complexity is illustrated by the cross-section in Figure 25 but the localities have been selected so that these complexities may largely be ignored. All the localities lie on the NW limb of the downward-facing Kinlochleven Anticline, so that the stratigraphic succession consistently youngs to the northwest. Small-scale folds of several generations have to be taken into account in some parts of the exposures, if sedimentary structures are to be used to demonstrate the succession.

Locality 7 (NN 097605) Leven Schist – Glen Coe Quartzite (30 minutes). Parking at this locality is difficult; cars and coaches are best taken to the nearest lay-by to the east. The exposures are on the loch shore where it trends NE-SW, southwest of Callert Cottage. The western exposures are of garnet-schist showing a transition eastwards through dark, sometimes calcareous, semi-pelites and thin quartzites, representing the lower Leven Schist. These rocks are strongly deformed and care has to be taken interpreting the gross younging from the small-scale graded bedding. However, the first thick quartzites to the east contain consistent west-younging cross-bedding. Current directions, as in all the Lochaber quartzites, are polymodal and these highly feldspathic sandstones are interpreted as tidal-shelf deposits.

Locality 8 (NN 120610-127613) Glen Coe Quartzite – Binnein Schist – Binnein Quartzite (30 minutes). Park in quarry or lay-bys near NN 123611. The westernmost lochside exposures exhibit the lower beds of the Glen Coe Quartzite with typical west-younging cross-bedding but also pebbly beds, mud-flake breccias and slump-folding. On the headland to the east these quartzites are transitional to the Binnein Schist which from small-scale cross-bedding can be demonstrated to be older. The easternmost exposures similarly provide a transition into the feldspar-poor Binnein Quartzite which, from cross-bedding, can be shown to the older.

From the map and cross-section (Fig. 25 and inset) and from Fig. 24 it will be seen that the Glen Coe Quartzite displays a spectacular thickness change within the area of Loch Leven. The visitor can observe from this locality how the formation swells to a thickness of over 2000 metres on the south side of the loch, where the beds are sub-vertical and show no evidence of major structural repetition. Traced to the north-west, around two major folds, the formation thins to a few tens of metres and is entirely absent in its expected position east of locality 6. The Binnein Quartzite, on the other hand can be traced for many kilometres across and along strike with no demonstrable change in original thickness or facies. Its thickness does reduce some 10 km to the SE but the character of this quartzite is considered to persist as far as the Schiehallion district described in Itinerary V. These relationships are portrayed on Figure 24.

Locality 9 (NN 133614) Binnein Quartzite – Eilde Schist (20 minutes). Drive east to the lay-by at this grid point. On the shore below, cross-bedding in the white Binnein Quartzite can be used to demonstrate that it is younger than the schist to its east. This, the Eilde Schist contains, near its junction, graded silty beds and sedimentary dykelets confirming its stratigraphic position.

Locality 10 Eilde Schist – Eilde Quartzite Quartzite (45 minutes). This junction may be located on the hillside NE of the previous locality at about NN 140620 or, closer to the road, about NN 148620 east of the burn. At both localities it is possible, with care, to demonstrate from cross bedding in the quartzite, to the east of the schist, that it is older. More satisfactory exposures can be seen, however, if the excursion to locality 11 is undertaken.

The Eilde Quartzite is very similar in character to the Glen Coe Quartzite, and the Eilde Schist is similar to the Binnein Schist. Anderton (1985) interpreted the two quartzites as tidal shelf deposits with the schists representing deepening and lower energy conditions. The Eilde Quartzite loses its separate identity outside the Loch Leven area, although elsewhere (e.g. the Schiehallion area of Itinerary V) it may be represented by quartz-rich facies at the top of the Eilde Flags.

Locality 11 (NN 200615-203610) Eilde Quartzite – Eilde Flags. This locality requires 2 – 3 hours to do it justice, but the whole river section from the old road bridge (NN 192618) (parking) eastwards may be used as a substitute for localities 9 and 10 above. Vertical Binnein Quartzite with westerly younging cross-bedding is well seen above the old bridge, and 200 metres upstream the junction with the Eilde Schist can be located; a spectacular fold of this junction (the Kinlochleven Antiform) may be seen on the hills both to the north and south. The Eilde Quartzite, interbedded with Eilde Schist first appears at about NN 200615; again westerly younging across the steeply dipping transition zone may be easily demonstrated.

If the above exposures are to be missed the visitor should keep to the path on the north bank of the river until the base of the Eilde Quartzite is reached about NN 203610. This is easily located by the overflow channel from the pipe-line which joins the river at a sharp bend. The quartzite is underlain (stratigraphically) by a transition zone of pelites with ribs of Eilde Flag-type psammite. Near the base of this zone is a 5m-thick unit of pebble (mostly K-feldspar) beds and slump horizons. The first flaggy psammites which characterise so much of the Eilde Flags are seen a further 300m upstream. Cross-bedding (10-30cm scale) consistently youngs west across the boundary. (Two to three hours).

This junction is most important in Dalradian stratigraphy, marking the boundary between the Appin and Grampian Groups. There have been suggestions that it marks the junction between rocks that suffered different tectono-metamorphic histories. However, it can be established at this locality that there is a sedimentary transition between the Eilde Quartzite and Flags with similar sedimentary characteristics on either side, that there is no tectonic break and that the rocks have suffered a united tectonic and metamorphic history.

ITINERARY V

Appin Group, Schiehallion District

J. E. TREAGUS

Maps: Geological map Treagus (1987);
Ordance Survey 1:50,000 sheet 51.

This excursion provides the opportunity to examine the Appin Group and the lower part of the Argyll Group in the Central Highlands, where the deformation is stronger and the metamorphism of a higher grade than that seen on the west coast. The most striking contrast between the two areas is the abbreviated nature of the succession at Schiehallion, especially that of the quartzite/pelite sequence of the Lochaber subgroup, compared with that seen in the east of the Loch Leven area (see Fig. 24). The other striking feature is that the lithological character of most formations is remarkably similar in the two areas, a fact which has allowed the correlation between them to be confidently made (Treagus and King, 1978) (see Fig. 24 and Table 4). Whilst the strength and complexity of the deformation has undoubtedly played a part in the abbreviation of the succession, the author would claim (e.g. Treagus, 1987) that the survival of sedimentary textures and structures in the Schiehallion area, as well as the absence of sedimentary discontinuities, suggests that this was a truly abbreviated sedimentary equivalent of the Loch Leven succession. Indeed, the very absence of thick members within this succession must have contributed to the intensity of the folding.

The intervention of an area of tectonic complexities and post-orogenic intrusives between the Loch Leven and Schiehallion areas obscures their stratigraphic and structural continuity. However, in the structural interpretation of Roberts & Treagus (1977b, fig. 3) the Loch Leven area would originally have lain several tens of kilometres to the NW, across the strike of the sedimentary prism. The contrast in thickness of formations, yet the absence of facies changes between the two areas, indicates steady and relatively rapid subsidence in the Loch Leven area, perhaps fault-controlled as suggested by Anderton (1985), here downthrowing to the NW.

The Schiehallion area is structurally quite complex, but exposures in the main excursion have been chosen so that the succession is seen right-way-up in descending order (Figure 26). However, it has to be remembered that the rocks have suffered two episodes of severe deformation expressed in both major and minor folds, and this may affect the facing direction of sedimentary structures observed in the field. The general relationship of the exposures to these structures is illustrated in the inset to Figure 26, but for further details see Treagus, (1987).

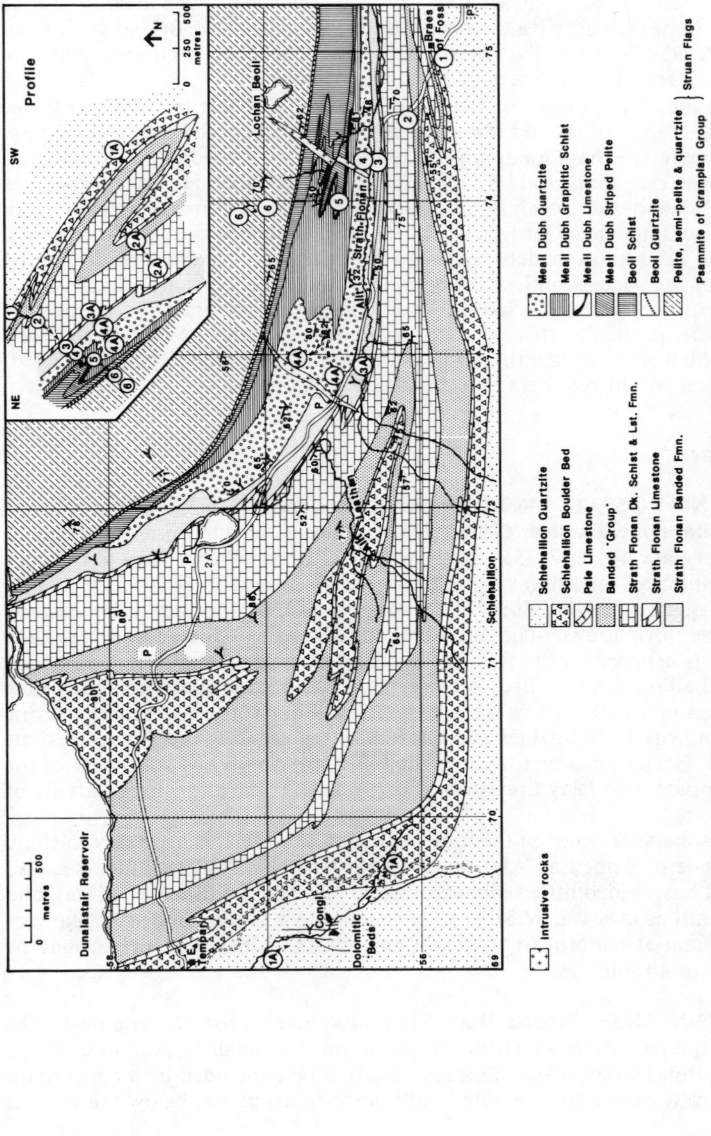

Figure 26. Map of the Schiehallion area for Itinerary V. Some typical strikes/dips of bedding are shown as well as localities where the younging of formations has been observed (Y symbols). Inset shows a schematic profile of the major folds, and the approximate level of localities. (After Treagus and King, 1978).

If travelling directly from Loch Leven, the quickest route is via the A82 to near Killin, the A827 to Kenmore at the head of Loch Tay and then minor roads north towards Tummel Bridge. At NN 776543 a narrow road leaves the B846 across the area of Figure 26. The road is not suitable for coaches. From Edinburgh or Perth the area is best approached via the A9 and Aberfeldy. The nearest public transport is from Pitlochry (railway station) by bus to Tummel Bridge or Kinloch Rannoch. Access is generally unrestricted, but please make contact with the farmers at E. Tempar and Braes of Foss (via Aberfeldy).

The main excursion, described below, is intended to enable the observer to see the lithostratigraphy of the lower part of the Argyll Group and the whole Appin Group through to the Grampian Group below, in reasonably consecutive exposures. The excursion could be made in a good half-day. However, exposures are often not good and certainly do not offer the best opportunity to see clean outcrop and sedimentary features. An alternative excursion is, therefore, offered which, while using more widely separated localities and therefore rendering the continuity of the succession less easily appreciated, uses exposures that give the best opportunity of appreciating the sedimentary characteristics of the formations. In particular this excursion examines outcrops of the Meall Dubh Quartzite which allow its identification as the Appin Quartzite to be appreciated. This excursion would require a full day to do it justice.

Main itinerary

Locality 1 (NN 749559 to 746561) Schiehallion Quartzite, Schiehallion Boulder Bed, Pale Limestone, Banded 'Group' (45 minutes). Cars and mini-buses may be parked in car-park at NN 753557. Walk west past Braes of Foss farm to the edge of small plantation on south side of road. Between here (NN 749559) and an abandoned quarry at NN 746561 it is possible to examine very poor outcrop of the above formations. The Schiehallion Quartzite (fine grained, slightly feldspathic) is exposed to the west of the plantation and small outcrops of the tillite (Schiehallion Boulder Bed) with carbonate and rarer quartzite and granite clasts are seen up to 500 metres west of this. Small outcrops of tremolite-bearing carbonate and rusty semi-pelites and quartzites (representing the Pale Limestone and Banded 'Group') can be found on the hill slopes south and southwest of the quarry. Compare with Islay Limestone, Port Askaig Tillite and Jura Quartzite of Islay.

To see reasonable outcrop of the tillite with granite clasts it is necessary to climb to the east side of Cnoc nan Aighean at about NN 739557. The tillite, (see also Locality 1A) has yielded little sedimentological information (Spencer 1971a), and is generally rather massive. Weathered surfaces have a honeycombed appearance due to preferential removal of the carbonate clasts. A basal till origin may be inferred. Extra 40 minutes.

Locality 2 (NN 746561-746562 Dark Limestone and Schist (20 minutes). The abandoned quarry offers excellent exposures of this slightly graphitic calcite marble with thin graphitic and siliceous ribs. It is here intruded by a concordant basic sill, now a garnet-amphibolite. Walk north to exposures below the road at

NN 746562 of rusty graphitic and non-graphitic pelite and a second grey limestone. Compare with Lismore Limestone and Cuil Bay Slate of Loch Leven area.

Locality 3 (NN 743563) Strath Fionan Pale Limestone and Banded Formation (15 minutes). Descend 200 metres to the WNW to the burn to see dolomite marbles and thinly banded psammites and semi-pelites. The latter exhibit small-scale graded bedding (feldspathic bases, biotite-rich tops) which youngs up to the south (compare Itinerary IV, loc. 3, Appin Limestone, at Loch Leven).

Locality 4 (NN 743564-740565). Meall Dubh Quartzite and Graphitic Schist (45 minutes). Ascend hill to north of burn examining outcrops (to E and W) and loose blocks of gritty feldspathic quartzite. Note: strong stretching of pebbles disguises original size; cross-bedding (10 -20cm scale) seen in loose blocks. At 743564 the transitional junction with the graphitic schist above is seen, though here it is strongly deformed and the usual sedimentary structures are not well seen. Several concordant amphibolite sheets are seen in the graphitic schist, which itself is a featureless kyanite schist. Walk westnorthwest along the outcrop to 740565 for good kyanite crystals (please don't hammer, there is much loose material). Compare (especially thicknesses) with Appin Quartzite and Ballachulish Slate of locs. 4 and 5 at Loch Leven (Itinerary IV).

Locality 5 (NN 740565-739569) Meall Dubh Limestone and Striped Pelite, Beoil Schist and Quartzite (40 minutes). Walk and climb NNW across a number of ridges which locally expose tremolite schist, creamy carbonate, finely bedded semi-pelite and much amphibolite. The semi-pelites rarely can be shown to young south towards the carbonate, although they are tightly interfolded. The steep slope to the north comprises a muscovite-rich garnet schist (Beoil Schist) with the pure Beoil Quartzite coming in towards the top. This thin unit may be equivalent to the Binnein Quartzite of loc. 9 at Loch Leven but the thick local Glen Coe Quartzite of Loch Leven is missing. Compare (especially thicknesses) with Ballachulish Limestone, Leven/Binnein Schist, Binnein Quartzite, locs. 6-9, Loch Leven (Itinerary IV).

Locality 6 (NN 739569-738572) Struan Flags of Grampian Group or 'Young Moine' (45 minutes). A traverse northwards goes across, at first, poorly exposed banded semi-pelites and psammites with no visible sedimentary structures for 150 metres. As exposure improves on the top, a search of these more quartzitic psammites reveals examples of 10-20 cm scale cross-bedding, some grading and excellent slump folds. Allowing for the presence of tight folds the younging is southerly in this south-dipping sequence. The quartzitic psammites may be equivalent to upper quartzitic facies of the Eilde Flags seen at loc. 11 at Loch Leven, in which slump folds are particularly characteristic. The zone occupied by the Beoil Schist, Quartzite and banded semi-pelites/psammites has suffered particularly high strains and is referred to as the Boundary Slide zone. Elsewhere, along strike, formations in the Dalradian are cut out against this zone and attenuated within it. Compare with Eilde Schist/Quartzite/Flag sequence of loc. 11, Loch Leven (Itinerary IV).

Alternative itinerary (locs. 1A to 4A)

Locality 1A (NN 691570-697563) Schiehallion Quartzite, Dolomitic 'Beds', Schiehallion Boulder Bed, Pale Limestone (Fig. 26) (2-3 hours). From East Tempar farm (NN 690575, 3 km east of Kinloch Rannoch; parking is rather restricted), take the track south until the first wall is crossed, then head south for Tempar Burn (see Bailey & McCallien 1937 p. 95 for map and description). First exposures in the burn are typical fine-grained Schiehallion Quartzite, followed by 50 m of dolomite, tremolitic and calc-mica-pelites and semi-pelites (in the latter, grading youngs west): the Dolomitic 'Beds'. The next 300 metres of quartzite in which granite and quartzite clasts are scattered is interrupted by one conglomerate bed in which the clasts are well rounded. Take the side burn which enters the main burn some 250m above the conglomerate at NN 693566. Exposures of the Schiehallion Boulder Bed are well seen in this burn 100 metres below where it is crossed by the track and adjacent to the track itself. Granite, quartzite, marble and schist clasts of a great variety of size (up to ½m) and shape are exposed, most considerably modified by deformation. Quartzite clasts are the least deformed, granites have axial ratios of c.2:1, whilst schist pebbles are much more elongate at 8:1. Carbonate clasts form distinctive cavities in the rocks as a result of weathering. The granite of the clasts is not known in any part of the Grampian Highland Dalradian. Comparison should be made with the Port Askaig Tillite and Bonahaven Formation of the Islay excursion (Itinerary II).

If returning to E. Tempar down the track, divert east where track crosses a burn, to exposures of the lower, calcareous, Boulder Bed and the Pale Limestone near the forestry fence (NN 697567). Allow two hours for return journey from E. Tempar.

If a good day's walking (minimum 3 hours from E. Tempar) is sought and transport can be moved near to loc. 3A (e.g. NN 726566), follow the exposures of Pale Limestone and Banded 'Group' (see below) south, parallel to the forestry fence. At about NN 702560 strike east to Tom na Fuine (NN 711561) and descend to the road north-eastwards via ridges of well-exposed Pale Limestone, Banded Group, Dark Limestone and Schist repeated by folding (see Fig. 26).

Locality 2A (NN 711574-716573) Banded 'Group', Dark Schist and Limestone (1 hour). Drive east from previous exposure for 2 km; park in wide section of road at NN 710576 or other lay-bys to east. Good exposures in woods around NN 711574 of Banded 'Group' show small-scale ripple lamination, grading channels and sedimentary dykelets in banded pelites, semi-pelites and quartzites. Walk east parallel to road, crossing two outcrops of Dark Limestone and intervening Dark Schist, (a graphitic kyanite–staurolite–garnet schist). Especially good exposures of the Dark Limestone are seen on the knoll at NN 716573, and of Dark Schist, opposite, north of the road. The latter occur in the hinge of a major fold (see Fig. 26); sedimentary structures are difficult to observe and interpret. One hour.

Locality 3A (NN 728564) Strath Fionan Pale Limestone and Banded Formation (40 minutes). Walk (or park in quarry at NN 726566) east along road and head for prominent exposure south of road, at NN 728563, for excellent exposure (dolomite, phlogopite and tremolite schist) of this lower pale carbonate. Observe junction with Dark Schist to south. Return north towards the road where exposures both on the south side (opposite prominent quartzite crags) and on the north side (100 m along road to west) in banded semi-pelites show clear grading and cross-laminations younging south. 40 minutes.

Locality 4A (NN 728565-729568). Meall Dubh Quartzite (1 hour). The lithology and stratigraphic position of this quartzite has been crucial in the recognition of the lower Appin Group in the Central Highlands. Bailey & McCallien (1937) and Rast (1958) correlated it with the Schiehallion Quartzite and the Strath Fionan Banded Formation and Pale Limestone (loc. 3) with the Banded Group and Pale Limestone, respectively, beneath the Boulder Bed. Apart from the southerly younging referred to in loc. 3, good examples of younging towards the Banded Formation and away from the Meall Dubh Graphitic Schist can be found in these outcrops of Meall Dubh Quartzite. The lithological character of the quartzite (pebbly, feldspathic) also is in total contrast with that of the Schiehallion Quartzite (loc. 1) but very similar to that of the Appin Quartzite (loc. 3, Loch Leven, Itinerary IV).

Three outcrops in particular are noteworthy: by the roadside at NN 728565 the crags exhibit a channel structure younging south and some ambiguous cross-bedding; climbing northeast, above an east-west dyke, (NN 732567), the transitional junction with the Meall Dubh Graphite Schist can be seen, which cross-laminations and small-scale grading show to be older (compare transition beds between Appin Quartzite and Ballachulish Slate of loc. 3, Loch Leven); climbing on to Meall Dubh, to the northwest, (NN 729569) large exposures of quartzite show good cross-bedding (note: the younging in these last two outcrops is towards the NW on the short limb of a major fold). One hour.

From this locality, the excursion can be completed, either by continuing down the succession to join the main excursion at loc. 5 or, by climbing north directly to the Beoil Schist and Quartzite south of the fence at NN 730571, and on to the 'young Moine' psammites (see locs. 5 and 6 for lithologies).

ITINERARY VI

Grampian Group: Pitlochry – Loch Laggan – Spean Bridge

J. A. WINCHESTER & B. W. GLOVER
(with additional note by J. E. TREAGUS)

Maps: Geological Survey – currently being re-mapped
Ordnance Survey 1:50,000 sheets 35, 41, 42, 43.

This excursion examines the principal lithologies and sedimentary structures of the Grampian Group (or 'Young Moine'), and how they have been modified by deformation. En route it also takes in a unique rock unit thought to be in the Appin Group: the Kinlochlaggan Boulder Bed of inferred glacial origin.

The Grampian Group covers an area of approximately 4250 km^2 within the Grampian Highlands of Scotland. Extending from Glen Orchy in the southwest to near Elgin in the northeast, it thus forms one of the most extensive rock sequences in the Scottish Highlands.

Previous investigators assigned these rocks to the 'Moine Schists' on the basis of a superficial lithological resemblance (i.e. Bailey and Maufe, 1960) while more detailed mapping described the rocks underlying the Appin Group in the Lochaber area as 'Eilde Flags' and as 'Struan Flags in Perthshire (Bailey and McCallien, 1937).

These rocks were initially considered to form a monotonous flaggy psammite sequence because clear marker horizons were lacking and hence little attempt was made to subdivide them stratigraphically. Collectively referred to as the 'Central Highland Granulites', they were considered to form a single succession.

In recent years structural and stratigraphic studies have been undertaken in many parts of the Central Highlands. As a result of detailed mapping, dominantly migmatitic gneisses in the northern part of the Central Highlands were interpreted by Piasecki (1980) as an older basement (Central Highland Division) to the remaining rocks in the area (Grampian 'Division' or Group), but this interpretation has been disputed, and recent structural mapping (Haselock, 1989 pers. comm.) has suggested that at least part of the 'Central Highland Division' may be equated stratigraphically with parts of the Grampian Group. At the same time a local succession was established in Perthshire in a structurally complex area of Grampian Group rocks underlying the Appin Group (Thomas, 1980).

The Grampian Group thus comprises the continuous sedimentary sequence which underlies the Appin Group of the Dalradian Supergroup. Two types of boundary with the Appin Group are seen: usually the contact is tectonic (i.e. the Iltay Boundary Slide, Fort William Slide), but occasionally a conformable sedimentary transition is seen, notably in the River Leven Inlier (NN 203610). Recent work in the Glen Spean area has established a complete Grampian Group stratigraphy (Table 7), part of which may be tentatively correlated with the Strath Tummel succession in Perthshire (Thomas, 1980; Glover and Winchester, 1989).

The aims of this excursion are to demonstrate structure and environments of sedimentation.

This itinerary requires the use of private vehicles. The first sections are alongside the A9 trunk road northwest of Pitlochry.

Warning Traffic on this road is very fast. Exercise great care in walking beside the road or crossing it; where possible walk between the crash barriers and the outcrops.

The route turns off the A9 at Dalwhinnie, and continues to Drumgask on the A886, and then along the A86 past Lochs Laggan and Spean to Spean Bridge on the Fort William to Inverness road.

Locality 1 (NN 784671), Clunes Cut, A9 (1 hour). This locality is on the A9 18 km northwest of Pitlochry (Fig. 27). An excellent freshly-constructed cutting exposes deformed psammites assigned by Thomas (1980) to the Tummel Psammitic Schist (part of the Strathtummel Succession) (Fig. 27). This succession forms the topmost part of the Grampian Group. At the southeast end of this road

SUBGROUP	GLEN SPEAN	SPEYSIDE	ATHOLL (A9)	
Glen Spean	Inverlair Formation		Strathtummel Succession	Kynachan Psammitic Schist Kynachan Quartzite Tummel Psammitic Schist Tummel Quartzite
	Clachaig Formation		Drumochter Succession	Psammitic and Semi-pelitic schist
Corrieyairack	Creag Meagaidh Formation			
	Monadhliath Schist/ Ardair Formation			
	Glen Doe Psammite	Glen Markie Psammite		
	Coire nan Laogh Semipelite *slide*	Ord Ban Rhythmites		
Ord Ban		Kincraig Limestone and Quartzite Succession (thin) *slide*		

Table 7. Summary of the stratigraphy of the Grampian Group. The Atholl sequence is after Thomas (1980).

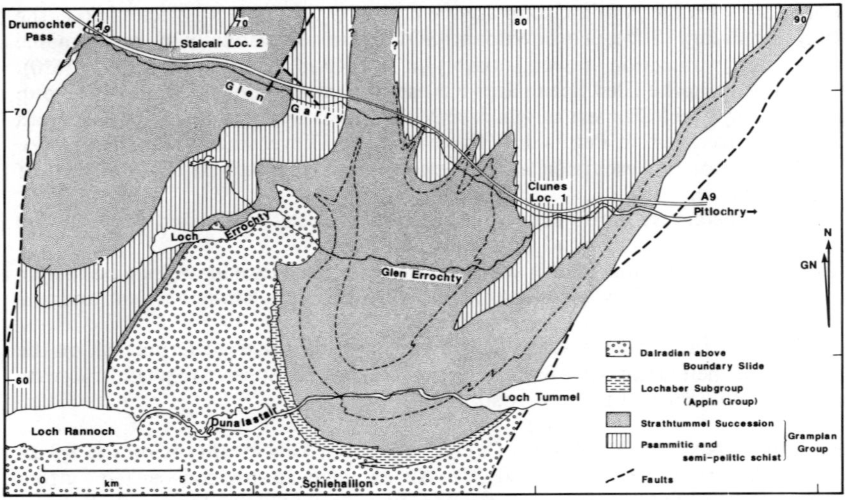

Figure 27. Itinerary VI. Stratigraphic map of the Grampian Group and overlying strata in the vicinity of the A9 road through Glen Garry. Note the position of Clunes road cut. Simplified from Thomas (1980).

Figure 28. Itinerary VI. Lithologies and structures in the Grampian Group (Strathtummel Succession), exposed in road-side exposures at Clunes in Glen Garry.

section the F_2 Clunes Antiform is exposed, and numerous minor F_2 'Z' folds are visible (Fig. 28). Sedimentary structures are preserved in many units, including cross-bedding (Fig. 29a; Fig. 281), through cross-ripple laminations (Fig. 28ii) and various water-escape structures including convolute bedding and sand volcanoes (Fig. 28iii). Younging directions show that the succession was inverted before D_2 deformation. Within the succession, biotite-bearing epidotic calc-silicates indicate that low amphibolite-facies conditions prevailed during the peak of metamorphism. Postorogenic cross-cutting dykes are abundant.
Continue along the A9 for 14km westbound to Locality 2.

Locality 2 (NN 672718) A9 Roadside, Stalcair Cut (Fig. 27) (30 minutes). A fresh road cutting on the north side of the dual carriageway A9, by a pylon buttress 150 metres east of a layby on the east bound carriageway, exposes Tummel Psammitic Schist. The section provides an excellent three-dimensional view of channels up to 3.5 metres in width (Fig. 28b). Internally these channels consist of dune-bedded white and grey psammites with numerous reactivation surfaces. Channel-fills also show dewatering and localised foreset overturning preserved in the sloping pediment. Interbedded with the channel-fills are ripple trough cross-laminated horizons with scarcer wave-formed bedding. This shallow water sequence is characteristic of the Glen Spean Subgroup.

Continue along the A9 to Dalwhinnie, then the A889 to Drumgask. The remaining localities on this Itinerary are shown in Figure 29.

Locality 3 (NN 614936) Drumgask (10 minutes). In a small disused quarry on the south side of the road junction of the A889 and the A86 (Fig. 30) migmatised psammitic gneisses are exposed. They are typical of the migmatites assigned to the 'Central Highland Division' by Piasecki, who considered them to form part of the 'Laggan Inlier' (pers. comm.).

Turn left along the A86 and proceed to the small village of Kinloch Laggan.

Locality 4 (NN 548898), Kinlochlaggan Boulder Bed (30 minutes). Enter Kinloch Laggan, passing the school and post office; park outside the village hall on the north side of the road. Walk back (east) to the roadside exposure between the hall and the track leading to the limestone quarry. This is the only substantial exposure of the Kinlochlaggan Boulder Bed yet reported, although scattered exposures have been found in the hills to the southwest (Treagus, 1969; 1981). Please do not hammer: the clasts are best observed by rolling back (and replacing) the blanket of moss and soil. The first exposures are of a psammite crowded with stones, 5-100 mm in length, of alkali granite, quartzite and semi-pelite. The clasts are oblate spheroids flattened in the cleavage (sub-parallel to bedding), around which the bedding lamination can rarely be seen to be deflected in the more easterly exposures. The occurrence of occasional large isolated clasts in a laminated matrix strongly suggests a glacial origin for these rocks, probably by iceberg rafting.

The stratigraphic position of this formation is obscure. Treagus (1969) noted the similarity of the granite clasts to those of the Schiehallion Boulder Bed (Loc. 1 and 1A, Itinerary V) at the base of the Argyll Group. However, he considered that the quartzite-pelite (with local tillites) – limestone succession at Kinlochlaggan

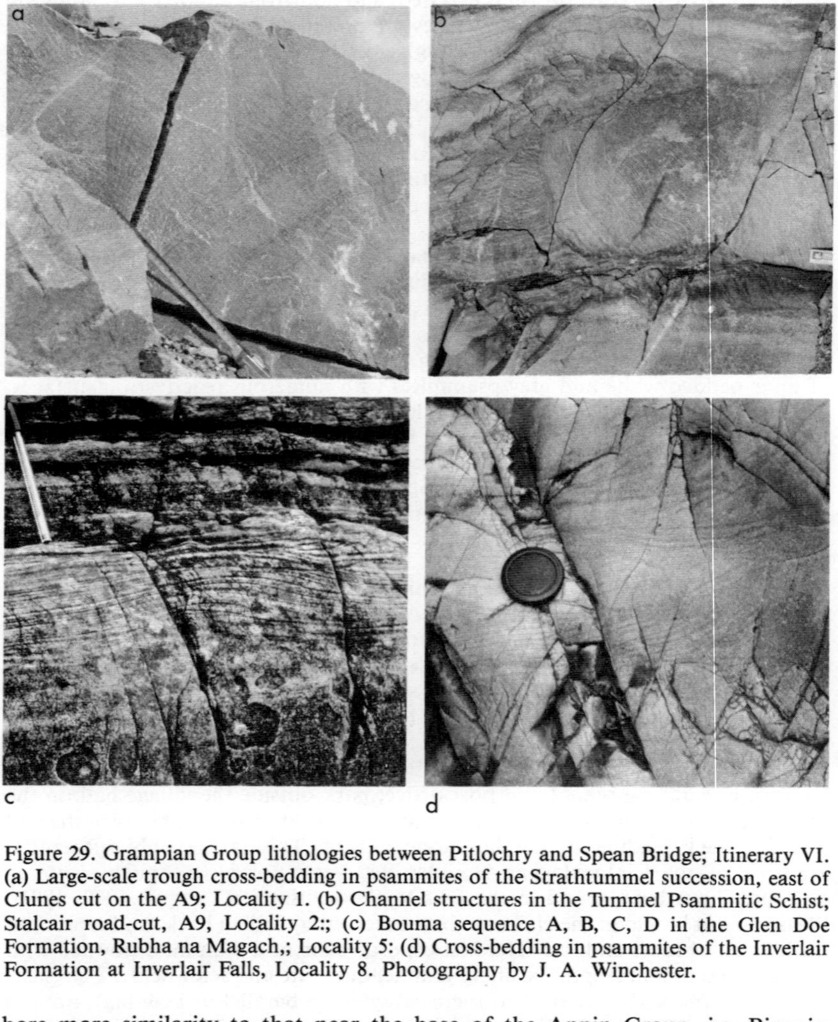

Figure 29. Grampian Group lithologies between Pitlochry and Spean Bridge; Itinerary VI. (a) Large-scale trough cross-bedding in psammites of the Strathtummel succession, east of Clunes cut on the A9; Locality 1. (b) Channel structures in the Tummel Psammitic Schist; Stalcair road-cut, A9, Locality 2:; (c) Bouma sequence A, B, C, D in the Glen Doe Formation, Rubha na Magach,; Locality 5: (d) Cross-bedding in psammites of the Inverlair Formation at Inverlair Falls, Locality 8. Photography by J. A. Winchester.

bore more similarity to that near the base of the Appin Group, i.e. Binnein Quartzite, Binnein/Leven Schist, Ballachulish Limestone, (cf. locs. 6 and 8, Itinerary IV) with the tillite horizon approximately coincident with that of the local Glen Coe Quartzite.

This locality also contains the totally recrystallized Kinlochlaggan Limestone. Together they occur within an isoclinal synform which is one of a series of folds within the Geal Charn – Ossian steep belt. Recent detailed mapping has shown that numerous tectonic slides within the steep belt isolate areas of the local

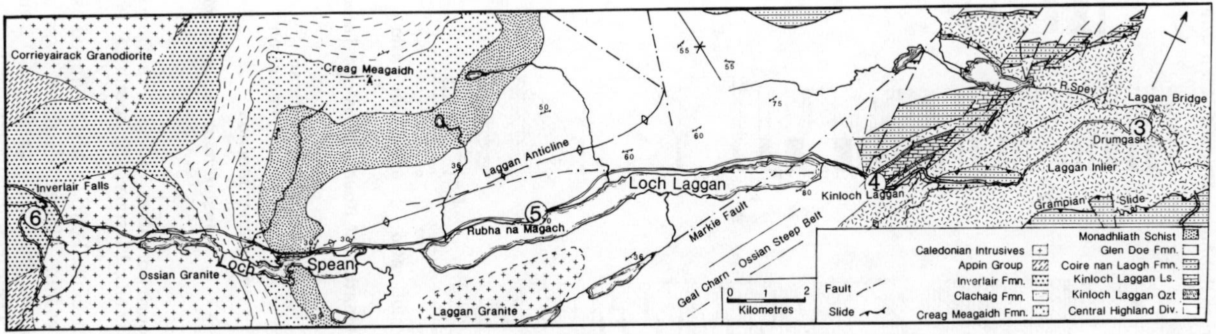

Figure 30. Stratigraphy of the Grampian Group in the Loch Laggan district, Itinerary VII. Mapping after R. Giles, B. W. Glover, C. T. Okenkwo M. A. J. Piasecki, S. Temperley and J. A. Winchester.

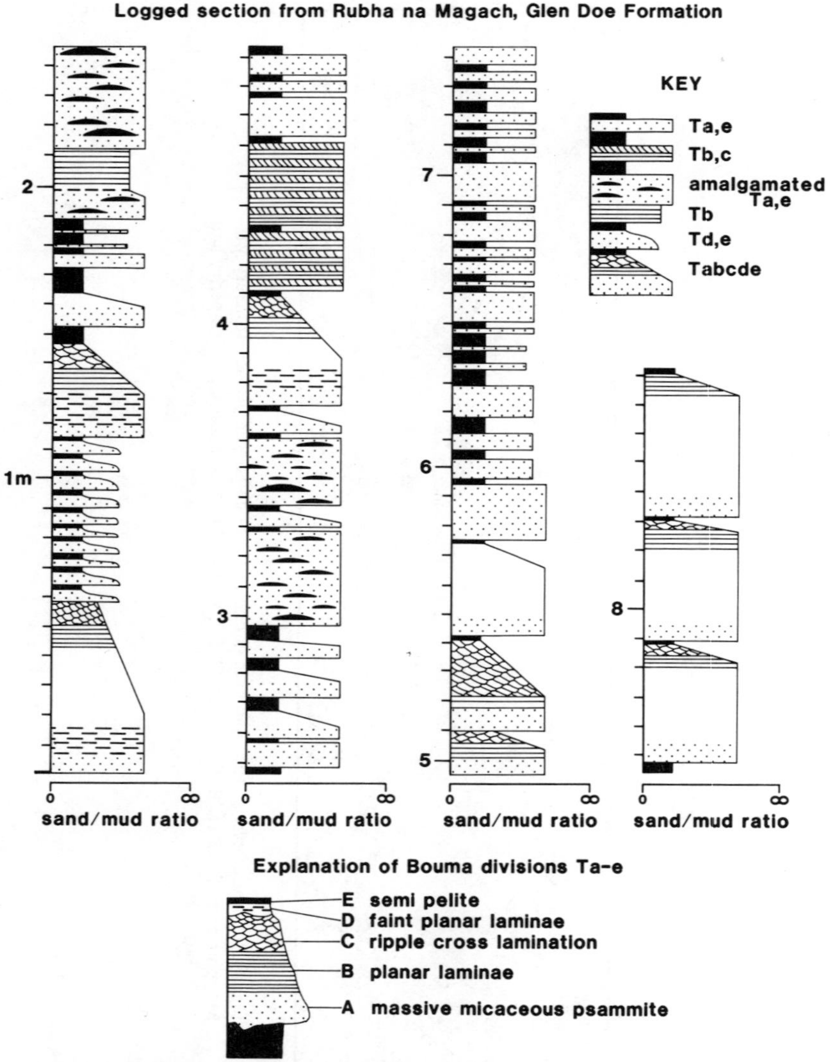

Figure 31. Logged section through turbidites of the Glen Doe Formation, Rubha na Magach, illustrating Bouma divisions, Itinerary VII, Locality 5.

succession that are hard to correlate. Pelitic schists mapped as part of the Central Highland Division occur within 200m of these exposures; thus, if the Kinlochlaggan succession forms part of the Appin Group, some 10km of Grampian Group rocks have been tectonically removed.

From Kinloch Laggan take the A86 southwestwards, passing along the shore of Loch Laggan to Rubha na Magach.

Locality 5 (NN 460849), Rubha na Magach (45 minutes). Park in the layby formed by a curve of the old road above the loch shore. Exposures of Glen Doe psammite (here over 3000 metres thick) occur on the shore of Loch Laggan. The Glen Doe Psammite is the thickest formation of the Corrieyairack Subgroup (Glover and Winchester, 1989) and consists dominantly of a series of turbiditic greywackes deposited in a fault-controlled marine basin. At Rubha na Magach extensive outcrop is exposed when the water level is low. The local succession forms part of the southeast limb of the D2 Laggan Anticline, and bedding/foliation dips are 60° southeast. Abundant sedimentary structures are preserved, including convolute bedding and ripple-drift cross-lamination (Fig. 29C). Turbidites exhibiting Bouma sequences can be recognized (Fig. 31). Abundant calc-silicate lenses, of probable concretionary origin, contain the assemblage garnet-hornblende-clinozoisite-andesine-quartz and indicate that low amphibolite-facies conditions prevailed during the peak of Caledonian metamorphism (Winchester, 1974).

The metasediments are cut by numerous post-orogenic dyke suites forming part of the 'Laggan Complex'. They include pink felsites (seen best in the cutting about the road) and several suites of pegmatite, including both pink and white megacrystic varieties.

If the level of Loch Laggan is very high similar features can also be viewed in the cuttings northwest of the road, although they are less clearly defined.

Locality 6 (NN 413821), Loch Spean (25 minutes). There is parking space by the boundary sign for Lochaber District. Roadside cuttings expose thinly-bedded micaceous psammites and semipelites of the Ardair Formation (Table 7). The Ardair Formation is the local name given a formation in Upper Glen Spean laterally equivalent to part of the Monadhliath Schist. At this locality thick semipelitic beds are locally present, as are well-developed whitish calc-silicate bands which usually contain the assemblage hornblende-bytownite-clinozoisite-garnet-quartz, sometimes with climopyroxene present. Small isolated calc-silicate pods up to 2cm long occur in micaceous psammite in an isolated outcrop at the west end of the section.

Locality 7 (NN 402818) roadside quarry 100m west of Allt na Uamha (15 minutes). In this quarry flaggy units of the Creag Meagaidh Formation (Glover and Winchester, 1989) are exposed (Table 7). They consist of planar laminated dark micaceous psammites associated with thin graded units usually 2-5 cm thick. Rare whitish calc-silicates are less than 3 cm thick.

Continue along the A86 across the outcrop of the Caledonian postorogenic Ossian Granite (exposed, exhibiting numerous xenoliths, in a large roadside quarry above the Laggan Dam at NN 372808) to NN 341809, then turn left down the small road (not suitable for coaches) signposted to Fersit. Cross the River Spean and park in the space on the west side of the road.

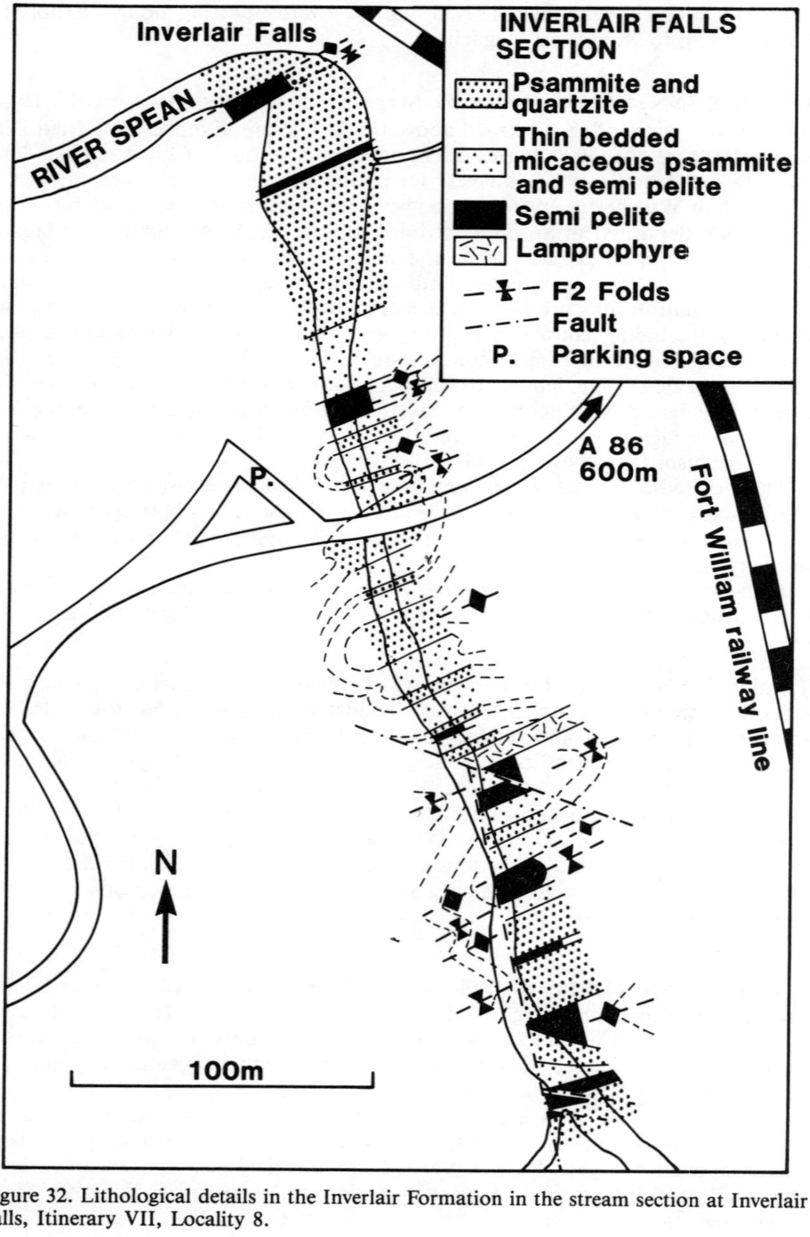

Figure 32. Lithological details in the Inverlair Formation in the stream section at Inverlair Falls, Itinerary VII, Locality 8.

Locality 8 (NN 341806), Inverlair Falls (1 hour). Exposed below the road bridge in the gorge and for 200 metres upstream are thick cross-bedded psammitic units erosively overlying thin semipelitic bands forming part of the Inverlair Formation (Glover and Winchester, 1989) (figs. 29d; 32). These units form a series of fining-upward sequences on a scale of several metres and have been lithologically equated with the Strathtummel Succession. They are currently interpreted as fluvio-deltaic and interdeltaic deposits laid down during the final stages of Grampian Group sedimentation. Several major units are exposed in the gorge above the Inverlair Falls. The succession is repeated in the gorge above the falls by several minor upright F_2 folds (Fig. 32). The Inverlair Formation is probably correlative with the Eilde Flags of the Loch Leven District (Glover and Winchester, 1989), (Itinerary IV).

Continue along the A86 towards Spean Bridge. An optional stop may be made at Roybridge to examine an exposure of the Appin Group Leven Schist, consisting of a silvery grey garnet-muscovite-biotite schist containing creamy calcareous bands displaying prominent randomly-oriented hornblende porphyroblasts. These are best seen on the left bank of the River Roy 150 metres northeast of the A86 road bridge over the river (NN 272814).

ITINERARY VII

The Moine Assemblage, Fort William to Mallaig

J. A. WINCHESTER
(with additional notes by M. J. HAMBREY)

Maps: Geological Survey Sheet 61; Strachan 1985, Powell 1974, Ordnance Survey 1:50,000 nos. 40, 41.

The purpose of this excursion is to exam the principal lithologies in the Moine Assemblage west of the Great Glen Fault along the A830 'Road to the Isles'. Localities displaying sedimentary structures are given most emphasis, but consideration of nature of deformation and metamorphism is also necessary. Indeed, tectonic complications to date have prevented the erection of a complete stratigraphic succession. Table 3 summarises the Moine tectono-stratigraphic sequence in this part of Inverness-shire and Figure 5 illustrates a structural cross-section that demonstrates the stratigraphic relationships between the main Moine Divisions. In this Guide reference is made to 'divisions' of the Moine Assemblage, although it has recently been claimed that the stratigraphic relationships between these divisions are now sufficiently understood for them to be classified as 'groups' (Holdsworth et al., 1987).

The itinerary begins with a consideration of the nature of the Great Glen Fault and the relationship between the Moine-like rocks of the 'Central Highland Division' and the Moine rocks of the Northwest Highlands.

The first Moine rocks to be examined belong to the Loch Eil Division, now considered to be the youngest of the Moine Assemblage and in stratigraphic continuity with the older Glenfinnan Division to the west (Strachan 1985, Roberts et al., 1987) (Fig. 33). Within the Loch Eil Division Strachan's mapping has distinguished an integral stratigraphic succession (Fig. 33). Almost all the formations recognized are psammitic, and three major folding events have been identified. The A830 road sections illustrate the nature of lithologies and structures within the Loch Eil Division, which is usually characterised by gently-dipping foliation and recumbent early isoclinal folding; hence the term 'Flat Belt' frequently applied to rocks of this section.

To the west, the Glenfinnan Division is exposed in this section within an area of Caledonian upright tight folding (D3) concentrated in a north-south belt centred on Glenfinnan known as the 'Steep Belt'. The boundary between the 'Steep Belt' and the 'Flat Belt' to the east has been called the 'Quoich Line' (Fig.

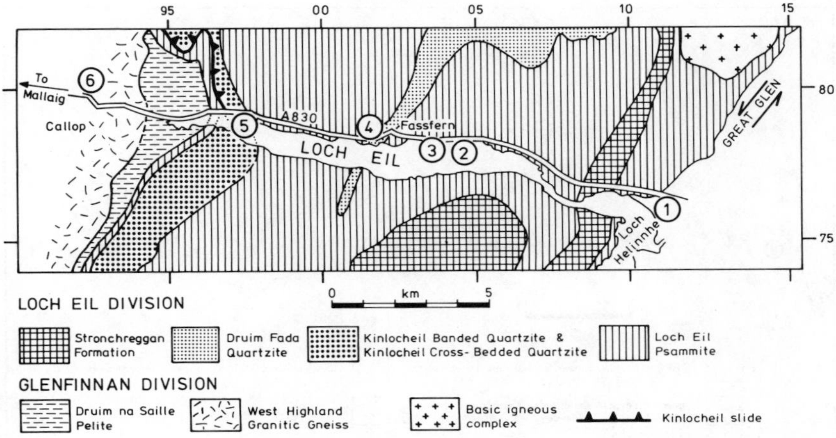

Figure 33. Itinerary VII. Stratigraphic map of the Loch Eil and Glenfinnan divisions of the Moine Assemblage between Fort William and Glenfinnan. Simplified from Strachan (1985).

5), which may represent a line of basement mobility, but which appears to have little importance in Moine stratigraphy. However, amphibolite bodies, such as those exposed at Fassfern, are most abundant along the Quoich Line, and several are exposed in the Allt Foinn Lighe north of the A830 (NM 960793). As a result of the D3 folding rocks of the Glenfinnan Division are exposed west of the Quoich Line. They consist of mixed semipelitic and psammitic rock-types, often intimately interbanded, and rare calc-silicate pods are also present. Coincident with the outcrop of the Glenfinnan Division is the axis of peak metamorphic grade in both early and late events. High amphibolite-facies conditions prevailed, with widespread migmatization in the more pelitic lithotypes. The combination of migmatitic segregations and high strain makes the preservation of sedimentary structures rarer than in the Loch Eil Division. Intruding the Glenfinnan Division are early amphibolites similar to those in the Loch Eil Division (Winchester, 1984), and major bodies of granitic gneiss collectively termed the 'West Highland Granitic Gneiss' (Barr et al., 1985). The granitic gneiss bodies are in turn cut by 'Caledonian' pegmatites and dark 'microdiorite' dykes of probable Ordovican age which sometimes show foliation developed in the final Caledonian tectonometamorphic event.

Separating the Glenfinnan and Morar divisions is the Sgurr Beag Slide Zone; in structural terms, it separates the Sgurr Beag (containing the Loch Eil and Glenfinnan divisions) and the Moine nappes.

The Sgurr Beag Slide Zone (Fig. 34) is crossed three times on the A830 road section. This repetition is attributed to late Caledonian folding of the slide zone, but there has been some recent debate about the timing of movement on the slide zone itself. Usually regarded as an early Caledonian feature, the slide zone has been found to include strained pegmatites which have yielded pre-Caledonian

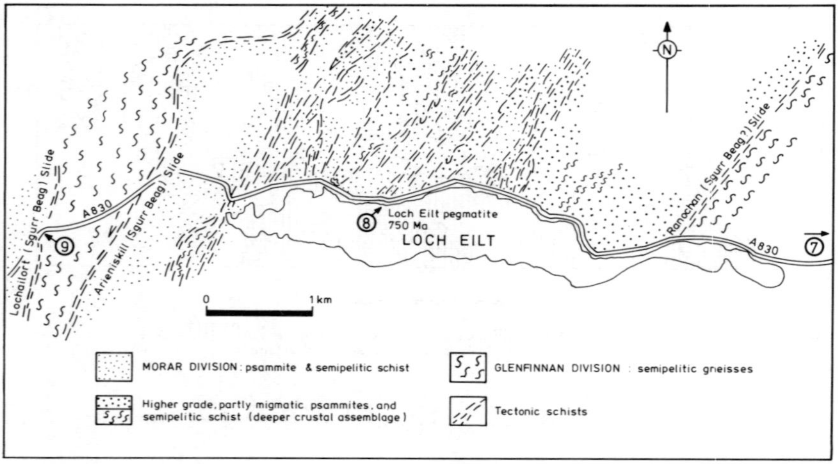

Figure 34. Itinerary VII. Sketch map of the Sgurr Beag Slide Zone, separating the Glenfinnan and Morar divisions, in the vicinity of Loch Eilt.

ages. These isotopic dates (van Breemen and Piasecki, 1983 pers. comm.) have also raised the possibility that several slides, rather than a single refolded slide, may be present. Their findings are not, however, widely accepted, as their argument depends upon the pre-Caledonian pegmatites being restricted to, and hence related to the generation of high strain zones. At the east end of Loch Eilt the Sgurr Beag Slide (locally termed the Ranochan Slide) (Baird, 1982) occupies a hollow on the hillside and is poorly exposed at low levels. Dates obtained from pegmatites spatially restricted to the associated high strain zone suggest emplacement around 450 Ma. However, isotopic dating of muscovite books in the pegmatites within high strain zones adjacent to the Arieniskill and Lochailort Slides west of Loch Eilt (thought by Powell et al. (1981) to be folded extensions of the Sgurr Beag Slide) yielded ages of approximately 730 Ma (Piasecki and van Breemen, 1983). If these dates record pegmatite intrusion restricted to and contemporary with the development of shear zones, two periods of movement on the slide zone are implied, the earlier one corresponding in age to the insubstantial 'Morarian' (Lambert, 1969) or 'Knoydartian' (Bowes, 1968) late Precambrian event reported from Scotland, which could be contemporaneous with late Proterozoic events in Denmark and East Greenland. If, on the other hand, the 'Morarian' pegmatites are not restricted to the shear zones, only a single 'Caledonian' phase of movement on the Sgurr Beag Slide Zone is required.

The Morar Division has the best preserved sedimentary structures within the Moine Assemblage, and these are particularly well-displayed in psammites on the west coast between Arisaig and Morar (Fig. 35). The local stratigraphic succession, which youngs towards the west and is near vertical, is summarised in Table 3. All the localities described herein occur on the western limb of the Morar antiform, a D3 structure. The psammitic rocks of the Upper Morar Psammite

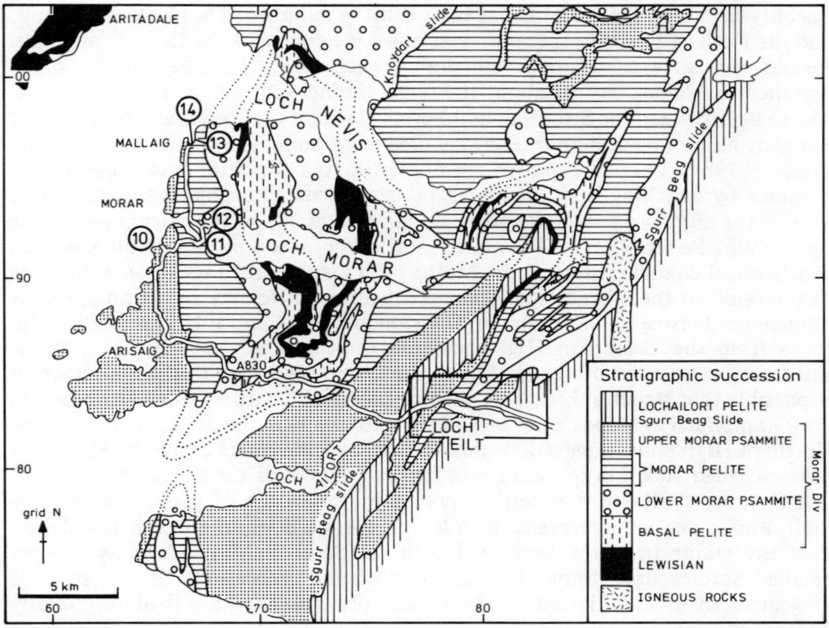

Figure 35. Itinerary VII. Stratigraphic map of the Morar Division between Loch Ailort and Loch Nevis. (Modified from Powell, 1974). The boxed area around Loch Eilt is shown in more detail in Figure 34.

were probably deposited in a tidal environment in the north of the area, and a possibly a fluviatile one in the south, although a shallow marine shelf model is favoured by Glendinning (in Allison et al. 1988). Calc-silicates occur as bands in the upper part of the Morar Pelite, and as lenses in the Upper Morar Psammite; the only basic igneous rocks are Ordovician microdiorite and Tertiary basalt dykes. The Tertiary igneous rocks reach their fullest developments in the isles of Eigg, Rhum and Skye which are clearly visible in fine weather from the coastline hereabouts.

Route

Take the road to Inverness from Fort William for 6 km then turn left along the A830 towards Mallaig. After crossing the broad flats of the Great Glen, roadside exposures reveal the lithologies, structures and metamorphic history of rocks from all three Divisions of the Moine Assemblage in the Northern Highlands. The road is two-lane as far as Lochailort with numerous lay-bys, then is mainly single track with passing places. A rail service operates between Mallaig and Fort William (connections to Glasgow) with two or three trains a day. The railway follows approximately the route of the road.

Locality 1. (NN 113768) The Great Glen Fault (5 minutes). The Great Glen Fault, and the Firth of Lorne to the southwest mark the course of the Great Glen Fault. Recognized early as a major sinistral wrench fault (Kennedy, 1946), much argument has since ensued about the scale, timing and direction of movement. The match between the Strontian and Foyers granodiorites originally proposed by Kennedy has not been supported by detailed work on these intrusions (Brown and Locke 1979), and an alternative correlation across the fault was subsequently obtained by matching the Caledonian pattern of metamorphic overprinting (the axes of the high and low grade areas are inclined at 30° to the orientation of the fault) (Winchester, 1973). This match is also supported by the lithological and geochemical characteristics of the Moine (and 'Moine-like') rocks on either side of the fault, as there is no significant geochemical difference in the analyses for 25 elements between the Glenfinnan Division and the 'Central Highland Division' rocks from the Grampian Highlands. On these grounds a post-metamorphic sinistral displacement of about 160 km is inferred, and with this displacement it is possible that structural features such as the Geal Charn–Ossian steep belt in the Grampian Highlands may be linked with the Glenfinnan steep belt in the Northern Highlands. Suggestions that the scale of movement along the Fault may have exceeded 2000 km in Late Devonian-Carboniferous times (e.g. van der Voo and Scotese, 1981) are thus not supported by the match of geology across the fault, and it may be interpreted as a less important zone of sinistral translation than the major fractures associated with the Scottish Midland Valley. Recent detailed studies have found few direct structural indications of the style of movement in rocks adjacent to the Great Glen Fault, which is almost totally unexposed.

Continue west along the A830, driving through Corpach and past the entrance to the Loch Eil Outward Bound Centre to Locality 2.

Locality 2 (NN 046784), Loch Eil Psammite (Loch Eil Division–30 minutes). Roadside cuttings reveal flat-lying psammites which are refolded by highly-attenuated D_1 structures. Three folds carry an axial-planar S_1 mica fabric and have north-south trending axes. Amphibolite-facies metamorphic conditions are indicated by the assemblage garnet-hornblende-clinozoisite-quartz-andesine in the calc-silicate rocks seen sporadically throughout the section. These calc-silicates tend to have a lensoid shape and are thought to be metamorphosed calcareous concretions of diagenetic origin.

1 km further west are more roadside cuttings (Locality 3).

Locality 3 (NN 036784) Loch Eil Psammite (Loch Eil Division) (15 minutes). At the east end of this locality a tight D_2 fold closure is present. Originally recumbent, it has been warped downwards by later D_3 deformation into a moderately-inclined attitude. Well-preserved sedimentary structures are displayed: both trough and tabular bedded cross-stratification and cross-lamination are abundant within the psammite, and thin bands of semipelite are present. Current directions appear to be strongly bidirectional (Fig. 36a), perhaps indicative of deposition within an environment subject to tidal activity (estuarine or shallow marine).

Continue west along the A830 for 1 km, then take the small road signposted Fassfern. Follow it for 500 metres, then park near the bridge over the river (Allt Suileag). Walk north for about 400 metres up the left bank of the river to Locality 4.

Locality 4. (NN 022793) Fassfern Amphibolites in Druim Fada Quartzite (Loch Eil Division) (30 minutes). Exposed in the bed of the Allt Suileag (allt=stream) are massive amphibolite bodies. Many of these bodies were intrusive tholeiitic dolerite or gabbro emplaced before the Precambrian D_1 deformation. Minor D_1 isoclines are exposed in the stream bed close to the right bank of the stream deforming the north contact of one amphibolite, which must have been emplaced prior to all deformation. Immediately to the south, in mid-stream, the amphibolite also occurs as blocks within a small explosion vent, thought to be related to the Caledonian (Ordovician) appinitic intrusions which are also present in the area.

Return to the A830 and continue west to Locality 5 near the head of Loch Eil.

Locality 5 (NM 970793), Kinlocheil Banded Quartzite (Loch Eil Division) (20 minutes). Roadside cuttings expose the Kinlocheil Banded Quartzite, which is the uppermost formation of the intermittently-developed and geochemically distinct lower part of the Loch Eil Division. Flat-lying feldspathic quartzites are exposed, cut by discordant granitic veins forming part of the 'Loch Eil Complex' of Fettes and Macdonald (1978). Two D_1 isoclines close to the west, separated by an indistinct east-closing fold. Their geometry is picked out by a thin biotite-rich semipelite bed, cut and partly followed by a highly-attenuated foliated microdiorite body, which was nonetheless probably intruded after most shearing was complete. The banding within the quartzite becomes discontinuous to the west: Strachan (1982) interpreted this as a product of shearing associated with the locally-significant D_1 Kinlocheil Slide, which may be seen away from the road at (NM 963802).

Continue west along the A830, crossing the outcrop (poorly exposed by the road) of the Druim na Saille Pelite, which is locally the uppermost formation of the Glenfinnan Division (Roberts et al., 1987). After passing under the railway bridge, continue for 600 metres and examine the large road cuttings at Locality 6.

Locality 6 (NM 919800), Ardgour Granitic Gneiss (30 minutes). Large roadside cuttings extending for 400 metres expose the Ardgour Granitic Gneiss, which is the best-documented part of the West Highland Grantitic Gneiss (Barr et al., 1985) (Fig. 36b). A Rb/Sr date of 1028 ± 43 Ma. for this gneiss (Brook et al., 1976) has been recently questioned (Rogers, 1989 pers. comm.), who was unable to obtain similar ages using modern isotopic methods. However, this migmatitic gneiss, which has moderately sharp contacts with the Glenfinnan Division metasediments exposed elsewhere, is believed by most to be a pre-orogenic granite, although the theory that it originated as a metasomatic derivative from the metasediments is still supported by some. At this locality the S_2 gneissic foliation is deformed by later folds and intruded by dark, cross-cutting microdiorite dykes (Smith, 1979) and several cross-cutting late Caledonian pegmatites.

a
b
c
d
e

Continue west through Glenfinnan Village along the A830 until the watershed between the Allt a'Ghiubhais and Loch Eilt is reached. Park on the road verge at the top, or continue for 200 metres along the road to a layby at (NM 857813).

Locality 7 (NM 859815), Beinn an Tuim Striped Schists, Glenfinnan Division (1 hour). Roadside exposures show little of the complex structures within the Beinn an Tuim striped schist, and it is important to climb to the small knoll immediately north of the road. Access is easiest from the southeast side, and on the northeastern slope of the knoll are glaciated pavements exposing a striped lithology consisting of alternating thin psammite and semipelite beds. Complex fold interference patterns and occasional sheath folds are well-displayed: many of the tight asymmetric minor folds verge towards the southwest, being parasitic to the nearby major F_3 Sgurr a'Muidhe Synform. Variations in style of these folds may be explained by the varying ductility of the different lithologies being deformed. Early quartz veins, thin foliated pegmatites and massive coarse-grained 'Caledonian' pegmatites all cut the metasediments. No sedimentary structures are preserved in this highly-strained area. Rare calc-silicate pods, with garnet-salite-hornblende-anorthite-quartz assemblages indicate high amphibolite facies (sillimanite zone) metamorphism.

Continue west along the A830 by the shore of Loch Eilt past Ranochan to a prominent outcrop on the south side of the road.

Locality 8 (NM 812827), Loch Eilt Pegmatite (Morar Division) (20 minutes). This outcrop is a classic locality and should not be hammered. It consists of a foliated beryl and apatite-bearing pegmatite and yielded muscovite Rb-Sr dates of 730 ± 20 Ma (van Breemen et al., 1974). It forms part of the 'Morarian' pegmatite suite often associated with high strain zones in the Morar Division rocks of the Loch Eilt Antiform exposed by Loch Eilt (Fig. 34).

Continue west along the A830 for 4 km and park by an electricity substation on the south side of the road at Locality 9.

Locality 9 (NM 772827), The Lochailort Slide Zone (40 minutes). Evidence of increasing eastward strain is displayed in Upper Morar Psammite in roadcuts situated 200 metres west of the electricity substation. At the west end of the roadcuts small-scale, flattened cross-lamination is barely discernable in thin psammitic units, and all trace of sedimentary structures rapidly disappears towards the east. Quartz 'plates' become more abundant eastwards, and immediately to the northeast of the electricity substation small-scale isoclinal folds which deform these quartz plates may be seen (Fig. 36c). This highly-

---

Figure 36. Lithologies and sedimentary structures in the Moine Assemblage, Itinerary VII. (a) Cross-stratification in the Loch Eil Psammite (Loch Eil Division), Locality 3. (b) Migmatitic gneiss of the Ardgour Granitic Gneiss with cross-cutting pegmatite vein, Locality 6. (c) Isoclinally folded quartz 'plates' in the Upper Morar Psammite (Morar Division), Lochailort Slide Zone, Loc 9. (d) Flaser-bedded psammites of the Upper Morar Psammite, Rubha'n Achaidh Mhoir, Morar, Locality 10. (e) Cross-bedding in the Upper Morar Psammite, Locality 10. Photography: (a) and (c) J. A. Winchester; (b), (d) and (e) M. J. Hambrey.

strained psammitic schist (Upper Morar Psammite) is followed immediately to the east by an internally unstructured semipelitic tectonic schist which contains small almandine garnets with the lilac pink to purple colouring typical of garnets within the Glenfinnan Division. The semipelitic formation exposed here at the structural base of the Glenfinnan Division is the Lochailort Semipelite, folded down in the core of the Glenshian Synform. To the west of this locality all Moine Assemblage rocks form part of the Moine Nappe and consist exclusively of Morar Division psammites and semipelites.

Beyond Lochailort the mainly single track road passes through Arisaig, where excellent exposures of Upper Morar Psammite, with cross-bedding suggestive of either fluviatile or shallow marine shelf deposition (Glendinning, in Allison et al., 1988) may be visited. The nest stop in this itinerary, Locality 10, is 3 km by road southwest of Morar Station.

Locality 10 (NM 662920), Upper Morar Psammite (Morar Division), north end of sandy beach south of Rubh'an Achaidh Mhoir (1 hour). (MJH). Parking is difficult in the vicinity of this locality, but it may be possible on the west verge where the road crosses a small stream, just past the track on the right to Glenacross. Otherwise, proceed to the estuary of the River Morar and walk back along the road. Cross a stile just south of the stream and follow the path through sand dunes to the beach. Outcrops occur north of the stream outlet as far as the point.

The rocks strike north-northwest and south-southeast and dip at a steep angle. They consist of medium-grained flaggy psammites with occasional thin semipelitic partings. The metamorphic grade, high greenschist facies – lowest garnet zone, is much lower than at localities east of Lochailort. Sedimentary structures are preserved, especially small-scale cross-bedding, flaser-bedding graded bedding and slump folds (Fig. 36d): the younging direction is to the west. Sediment derivation, as elsewhere in the Morar Division, is from a southerly quarter and the lithologies and sedimentary structures are consistent with a probably shallow-water (tidal) depositional environment. This contrasts with probably fluviatile deposition to the south near Arisaig, where planar sets of cross-bedding are developed (Fig. 36e).

Other instructive outcrops with well-preserved sedimentary structures (here also including folded cross-bedding) occur at the south end of the beach at (NM 657916).

Return to the road and proceed to the Falls of Morar where parking is possible in several places suitable for visiting localities 11 and 12.

Locality 11 (NM 681922), Morar Pelite (Morar Division), 1 km south-southeast of Morar Station, Falls of Morar (15 minutes). Exposed in the river draining Loch Morar and on the shore to the south are micaceous psammites and semipelitic schists assigned to the lower part of the Morar Pelite. The junction with the underlying Lower Morar Psammite is gradational and the change in lithology reflects an increased proportion of silty detrital material introduced at this time.

Locality 12 (NM 683925), Lower Morar Psammite, 900 metres southeast of Morar Station (15 minutes). Roadside exposures reveal the uppermost portion of this unit. These medium-grained pale grey quartz-oligoclase-biotite psammitic schists are less fissile than the Upper Morar Psammite. Calc-silicate lenses are absent, but small-scale sedimentary structures are occasionally visible, indicating westward younging.

Go along the A830 to Mallaig. Parking is possible in several parts of this fishing port.

Locality 13 (NM 680969), Morar Pelite (Morar Division) Mallaig Harbour – east (10 minutes). This locality (and Locality 14) are both well described in the Guide No. 35 of the Geologists' Association (Lambert and Poole, 1964).

A small roadside exposure reveals a coarse-grained biotite schist with prominent dark purple almandine garnets up to 4 mm in diameter. Calc-silicate bands are absent. This rock forms the middle portion of the Morar Pelite and contains the only massive pelites in the Morar Division.

Locality 14 (NM 678969), Morar Pelite (Morar Division) Mallaig Harbour (30 minutes). 400 metres east-southeast of Mallaig Station is a road-cutting which exposes semipelites with subordinate psammite bands forming the upper part of the Morar Pelite. The succession youngs to the west: dips are vertical. Prominent pale calc-silicate ribs are present. These rocks are MgO-poor; hence they do not contain tremolite or diopside. Instead the assemblage zoisite-calcite-biotite-garnet-quartz-oligoclase is dominant, with rare hornblende occurring in those rocks with exceptionally high CaO/Al_2O_3 ratios combined with low CO_2 (Winchester, 1974). This mineral assemblage is typical of Kennedy's (1949) lowest zonal assemblage recognized in Moine calc-silicates and confirms the lower metamorphic grade in this area. Rhythmic sedimentation has been suggested for these rocks; the calc-silicates may have resulted from the diagenetic introduction of calcite into porous sandy beds, while adjacent impervious shales remained non-calcareous.

Quartz veining is common, and quartz boudinage occurs on horizontal axes. Three lineations occur on bedding surfaces: an early near-vertical mineral lineation, a second 'herring-bone' crinkling which dips at approximately 80° north and a third 'herring-bone' crenulation which has approximately horizontal axes.

Mallaig has a regular ferry service to Armadale on the Isle of Skye, operated by Caledonian MacBrayne. This provides a link with Itinerary VIII in the Sleat Peninsula. However, vehicles are not carried in winter and spring, and access to Skye with private transport has then to be made via the ferry at Kyle of Lochalsh.

ITINERARY VIII

'Torridonian' (Sleat Group) of Southeast Skye

A. D. STEWART

Maps: Geological Survey 1:50,000 Sheet 61.
Ordnance Survey 1:50,000 Sheets 32 and 33.

Arkoses of the Sleat and Torridon Groups, forming an apparently conformable sequence about 4500m thick, crop out over some 170km^2 of trackless waste in the Sleat of Skye, much of it covered with young conifer plantations. The base of the sequence is concealed by the sea but is known elsewhere unconformably to overlie basement gneisses, for example at Fernaig, about 10km northeast of Kyle of Lochalsh (NG 842336). The top of the sequence in Skye is unconformably overlain by Lower Cambrian quartzite, for example on the coast at Ob Gauscavaig (Fig. 37A) (NG 594121).

The rocks in the Sleat are part of the Kishorn nappe and have been thrust some 20km from the east (Ramsay 1969). At the same time they were slightly metamorphosed, turning their original red colour to green or grey. Sedimentary structures, however, are generally well preserved. Palaeocurrents come mainly from the west so that the Applecross Formation of the Torridon Group is noticeably finer than its counterparts on the 'foreland' in Rhum and Scalpay. Except in grain-size, however, the Applecross of Skye closely resembles that in other areas, and in particular contains the characteristic pebble suite of jasper, quartzite and porphyry. The Sleat Group is not known outside the nappe and so no comparisons with the 'foreland' are possible. It may have been deposited in a late Proterozoic sub-graben, compressed during Palaeozoic time and transformed into a nappe.

The Sleat Group differs markedly in composition from the Applecross Formation of the Torridon Group. Firstly, the pebbles and composite grains in the Sleat are almost entirely porphyry, of rhyolitic or rhyodacitic composition, with only a few acid gneiss pebbles to make up the total. There are none of the sedimentary and metasedimentary pebbles found in the Applecross Formation. Evidently the source areas of the Sleat and Torridon Groups were slightly different. Secondly, plagioclase in the Sleat Group is typically oligoclase-andesine, while in the Applecross Formation it is invariably albite, the result of diagenetic albitization. The Sleat Group becomes more mature upwards, quartz increasing fourfold at the expense of matrix, while plagioclase becomes less abundant and less calcic. This trend perhaps reflects retreat of the source area.

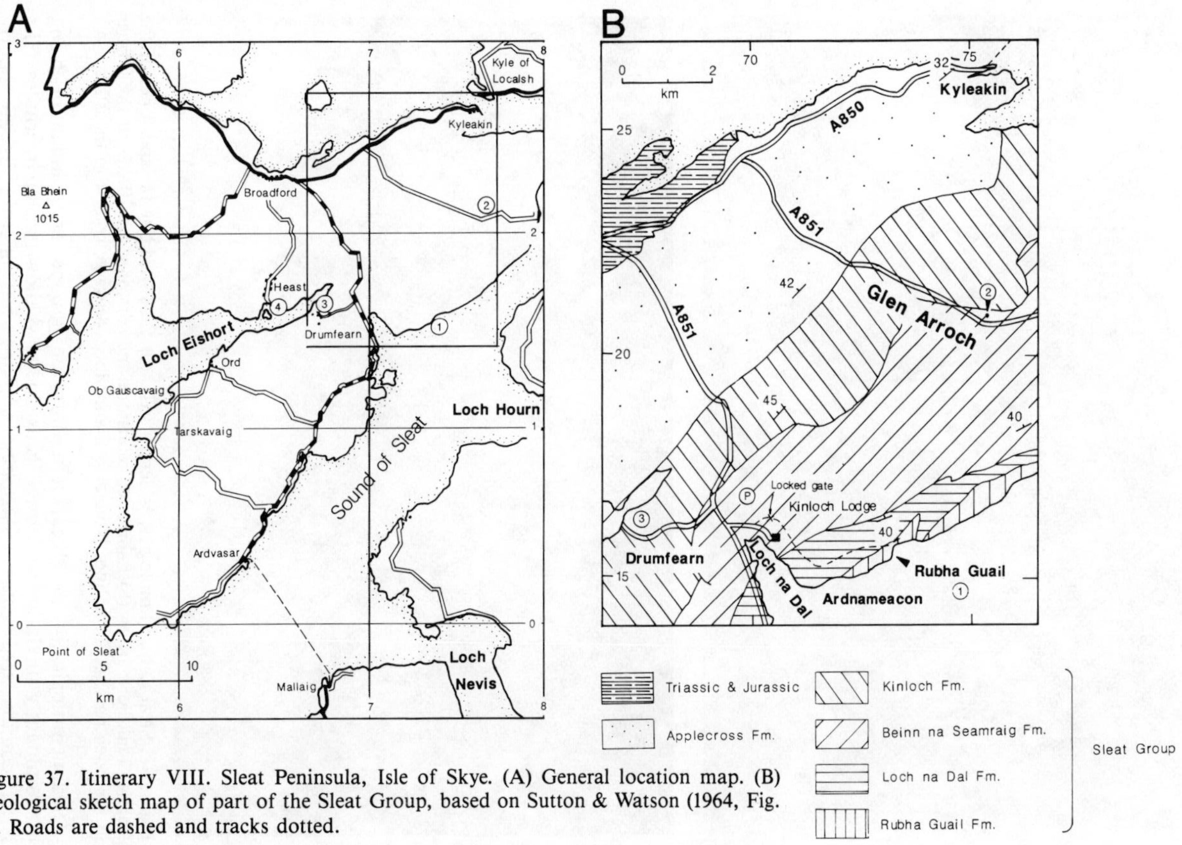

Figure 37. Itinerary VIII. Sleat Peninsula, Isle of Skye. (A) General location map. (B) Geological sketch map of part of the Sleat Group, based on Sutton & Watson (1964, Fig. 2). Roads are dashed and tracks dotted.

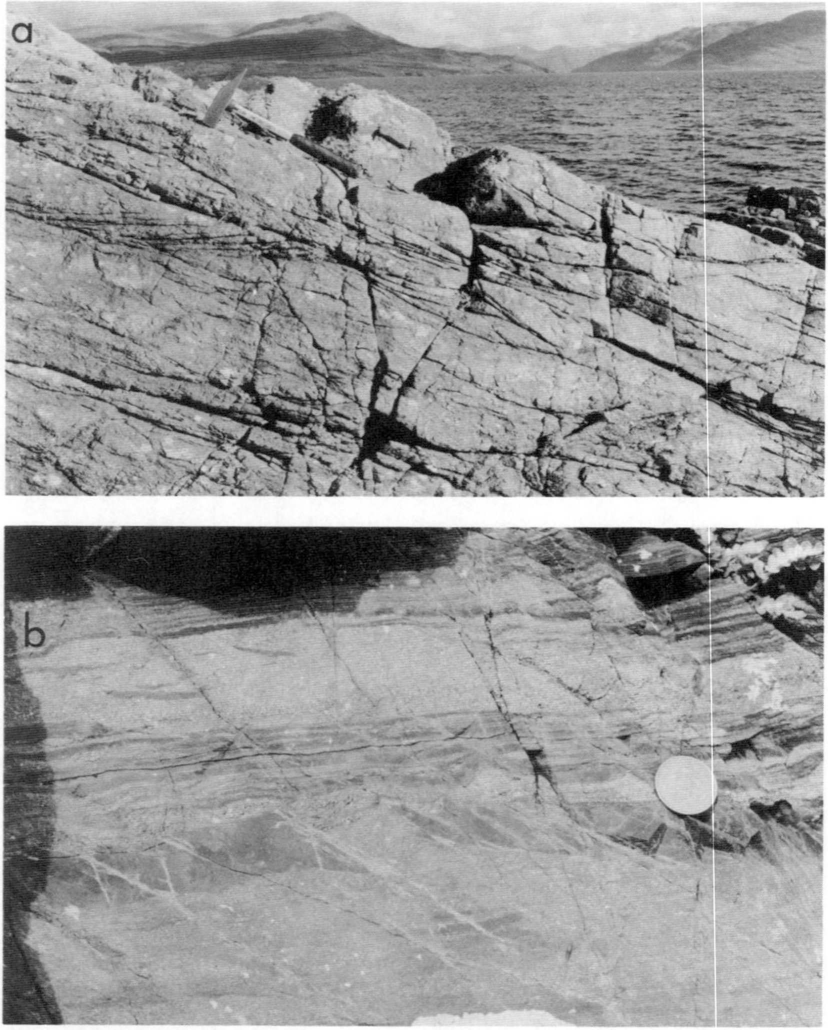

Figure 38. Sleat Group lithologies, Itinerary VIII. (a) Cross-bedding in sandstones of the Rubha Guail Formation. (b) Laminated mudstone and siltstone, with flakes of the former in the Loch na Dal Formation. Note also the inclined cleavage, related to thrusting.

Sedimentologically the Sleat and Torridon groups are similar in being predominantly fluviatile, with brief lacustrine or shallow marine interludes. The latter contain sedimentary phosphate laminae, but microfossils are poorly preserved. No isotopic dates are available for these rocks.

Two important papers dealing with sedimentary structures and palaeocurrents in the Sleat have been published by Sutton & Watson (1960, 1964). There is a similar study of the Applecross Formation (Torridon Group) by Selley *et al.* (1963).

Locality 1 (NG 733155). Type sections of the Rubha Guail & Loch na Dal Formations (c. 4 hours).

The section is best seen below half tide. Start from the locked gate which gives access to the Forestry Commission road about 0.5km northwest of Kinloch Lodge Hotel, and walk to the road end, very near the coast, 3km to the east. Scramble down to the beach at Rubha Guail (NG 733155). The 4km walk back along the coast from here to Kinloch Lodge Hotel crosses magnificent exposures of the lowest two formations of the Sleat Group; the Rubha Guail (250m thick) and the Loch na Dal (800m thick) (Fig. 37B).

The sediments just north of the point called Rubha Guail are grey mudstones and fine greenish-grey sandstones near the middle of the eponymous formation. Desiccation cracks are seen at several points; there is a particularly good exposure showing polygons in plan (Stewart, 1962, Fig. 11) about 120m north of the point, 25m east of high water mark (NG 73421565). Further to the northeast along the beach, stratigraphically lower and rather coarser beds are exposed. They also show the green tints typical of the formation, due to diagenetic epidote in the sandstone and chlorite in the mudstone. The sandstone beds have erosional bases and are internally trough cross-bedded (Fig. 38a).

They probably represent fluvial injection into a very shallow lake or sea which seems to have episodically dried out.

Southwestwards from Rubha Guail the section shows grey and green fine sandstone and millimetre-laminated mudstones. Sedimentologically these belong to the Loch na Dal Formation but were included by the Geological Survey in the Rubha Guail Formation, presumably because of the occasional green beds. About 200m southwest of the point (NG 73161544) a fault brings in the lower beds of the Rubha Guail Formation, mainly trough cross-bedded coarse green sandstones. Finer sandstones in this section often show syn-depositional diapiric disturbances. These coarse beds are thought to be alluvial fan deposits. They crop out along the coast to the west for a further kilometre.

The lowest beds of the Loch na Dal Formation are found near the mouth of the stream Allt an Teanga Odhair (NG 72201504), faulted against the Rubha Guail Formation. What may be regarded as the type exposure for these beds crops out on the shore 200m further west (NG 71971503). Millimetre and centimetre laminated dark-grey mudstone or siltstone is the main lithology here (Fig. 38b). Some laminae are notably enriched in sedimentary phosphate. Sedimentary veins are quite common but they do not have the convincing polygonal patterns seen in the Rubha Guail Formation. These sediments are believed to have formed in a perennial lake or shallow marine environment. Centimetre to decimetre thick units of medium to coarse grained sandstone interrupt the sequence (cf. Stewart 1962, Fig. 12). They are not usually cross-bedded, but some have sharp bottoms and graded or rippled tops. Texturally they are greywackes and may represent deposits of weak turbidity currents like those on a delta front, stemming from alluvial fans on the lake margin to the west.

The upper 200-300m of the Loch na Dal Formation are much coarser than those described above. They are first encountered on the beach near the house at Ardnameacan (NG 712149). The sandstones are very coarse, sometimes pebbly, with strongly erosional bases. The type exposure for these beds is on the beach about 0.5km southeast of the Kinloch Lodge Hotel (NG 70831541), stratigraphically about 130m below the top of the formation. The 20m section has at its top a well-sorted trough cross-bedded pebbly sandstone, 5m thick, with 0.5m of erosional relief at its base. Ripple-drift laminated fine to medium grained grey sandstone is another typical facies. Laminated mudstone, however, is rare. The pebbly sandstone is clearly a channel sand, cutting into sediments like those on a proximal delta front.

The upward-coarsening Loch na Dal Formation is regarded as a delta complex expanding eastwards into, and eventually over, a lake or shallow sea. By the end of Loch na Dal time in this area sedimentation was exclusively fluvial. Delta progradation, however, must have halted for quite long periods in order to develop such a substantial sediment thickness. Active faulting may have been responsible (*cf.* Stewart, 1982, Fig. 4).

About 100m northwest of the last locality (NG 70741547) metre-thick beds of coarse-grained grey sandstone appear. These belong to the Beinn na Seamraig Formation. The exposures continue along the beach past Kinloch Lodge Hotel but cleaner rock faces can be seen by the road at the head of Glen Arroch.

Locality 2 (NG 752207). The Beinn na Seamraig Formation at Glen Arroch (c.1/2 hour).

The road up Glen Arroch rises to a summit 3.5km west of Kylerhea village. About 150m north-east of the summit the Beinn na Seamraig Formation is splendidly exposed on a bluff 20m high (NG 75362087). This is near the top of the formation, which has a total thickness of 1200m.

The rocks are mainly medium to coarse grained, cross-bedded grey sandstones in metre-thick beds. Cross-bedding is both of the trough and planar types, and about half of it shows soft-sediment contortions which were eroded before deposition of the next bed. The bases of the sandstone beds are typically highly erosive. The tops, at least in other localities, frequently show ripple-drift lamination, developed as flow waned. The section also contains grey, laminated siltstones and rippled fine sandstones quite like those in the upper part of the Loch na Dal Formation. The only significant difference between the Beinn na Seamraig Formation and the upper part of the Loch na Dal Formation is the much higher proportion of channel sands (around 80%) in the former. Another difference, not readily appreciated from a single locality, is that the palaeocurrent vector-mean in the Beinn na Seamraig was due south, whereas during Loch na Dal time it was due east (Sutton & Watson, 1964, Fig. 8). This probably means that Beinn na Seamraig channels were constrained to follow the graben axis.

The base of the overlying Kinloch Formation is exposed on the mountain side 400m north of the section just described. However, there are more easily accessible exposures on the coast near Drumfearn.

Locality 3 (NG 671160). The Kinloch Formation at Drumfearn (1 hour). The upper part of the Kinloch Formation, which is 1200km thick, is exposed in the easily accessible coast section northwest of Drumfearn. From the road end (NG 671160) walk 200m down to the coast and thence 100m north to a small promontory (NG 67071629). The clean-washed 13m section shows fine and very fine grained sandstones, about 80% of which contains ripple-drift lamination. A third of the beds were contorted whilst still wet, and eroded before deposition of the following bed.

A further 180m along the coast to the north (NG 67131647) a second section displays 6m of similarly fine sandstones in beds 0.5-1m thick. The beds show contorted cross-bedding, overlain by undisturbed flat bedding (upper flow regime), or wave ripples.

These two sections represent the middle and lower parts, respectively, of major fining-upward cycles, the upper fine-grained portions of which have been ground down by Pleistocene glaciation along this portion of the coast and are now covered by shingle beaches. These cycles, 25-35m thick, compose only the upper 200-300m of the formation, but the sandstones in the two sections described can, nonetheless, be taken as representative of those in the formation as a whole.

Entire cycles can be seen on the coast 500m southwest of Ob Gauscavaig (Fig. 37A) (NG 588112) and elsewhere (Stewart 1966b). Roughly half of each cycle is sandstone, with a very sharp, erosive base. The other, fine-grained, half is composed of millimetre and centimetre-thick beds of rippled grey siltstone. Sand-filled cracks, possibly due to desiccation are common. These are the 'carbonaceous shales' in which the Geological Survey searched unsuccessfully for fossils (Geikie 1900, p.185).

The cycles are interpreted as alluvial fans interfingering with lake sediments. They are thinner versions of those forming the lower few hundred metres (at least) of the Applecross Formation north of the Loch Maree fault.

Locality 4 (NG 648166). The Applecross Formation (Torridon Group) near Heast (2½ hours).

The Applecross Formation, replete with soft sediment contortions, is excellently exposed along the coast for 2km from Heast road end (NG 648166) westwards to Torr Mor, where it is unconformably overlain by Cambrian strata (NG 627160) (Fig. 37A). There is a particularly good exposure 270m southeast of the Cambrian outcrop and 15m inland from high water mark (NG 62911595). Some 23m of sandstones can be conveniently studied here. The coarser sandstones have an average grain-size of around 0.25mm and belong to the 'fine-grained assemblage' of Selley *et al.* (1963, p. 226).

Roughly 40% of the beds show what appears to be upper flow regime flat bedding, resting on an erosion surface. On closer inspection however, many of the laminations can be seen to dip gently towards the southeast, relative to the erosion surface, *i.e.* in the palaeocurrent flow direction. Some of these surfaces may be true flat bedding but many of them must represent the bottom sets of large-scale cross-bedding, since the laminae traced up-dip tend to steepen and become contorted. There is also a tendency for the grain-size to increase slightly with the appearance of large-scale cross-bedding. This kind of small-scale cyclicity, in which a kind of flat bedding gives way upwards to contorted cross-bedding, occurs five times in the section. It occurs widely in both the Applecross and Aultbea formations.

The contortions are typically upward pointing cusps, with a wavelength of the order of a metre. Cusps increase in amplitude upwards through a bed and at the top are truncated by erosion. Rarely they penetrate the erosive base of the overlying bed (an example of this can be seen 15m above the base of the section) demonstrating that a single bed can sometimes be mobilized more than once. Cusp cores are often structureless, suggesting fluidisation of the sand by upward flowing pore water. In extreme cases the cusps in the upper part of a deformed bed are completely destroyed and only the synclinal lobes survive, floating in an apparently structureless matrix (Selley *et al.*, 1963, Figs. 4–6).

These sediments are interpreted as braided channel sands (Selley, 1965; Williams, 1969b), stemming from a humid highland source area. If the Applecross rivers were subject to very variable discharges one would expect, by analogy with modern rivers of this kind, to find abundant soft sediment contortions. Earthquake shocks can also produce contorted bedding. However, contortions affect half of all the beds in the section, and indeed the whole formation. It seems most unlikely that earthquakes could have been so frequent, and so a purely sedimentary origin for the contortions is preferred.

ITINERARY IX

Torridon Group and Lewisian Unconformity, Loch Torridon

A. D. STEWART

Maps: Geological Survey 1:50,000 sheet 81.
Ordnance Survey 1:50,000 sheets 24 and 25.
Ordnance Survey 1:25,000 Outdoor Leisure Sheet 8.

The Torridon district is the type area for the Torridon Group. The unconformable contact of the Group with the Lewisian basement has relief of about 300m, particularly evident along the southern margin of the loch. The lowest sediments (Diabaig Formation) are diverse, ranging from coarse gneiss breccia, through flaggy red sandstones, frequently rippled, into grey shales with desiccation and ripple structures. Both lateral and upward fining, away from the basement, can be detected. These sediments fill the lower parts of the pre-Torridon Group valleys and are overlain by the Applecross Formation which covers the rest of the ancient topography. The characteristic features of the Applecross sandstones are their red colour, very coarse grain-size, exotic pebble suite including porphyry, red jasper and quartz schist, and finally the highly contorted bedding. The pebble suite has been described by Williams (1969a) and the contortions by Stewart (1963) and Selley *et al.* (1963). The Applecross Formation is well seen on Ben Alligin and Liathach, to the north and east of Upper Loch Torridon respectively. It is about 3km thick and is unconformably overlain by the basal Cambrian quartzite on Liathach. Pebbles, although characteristic, are not abundant in this area. They may be examined best at Locality 6. The contact between the Diabaig and the Applecross is sometimes sharp, as at Ob Mheallaidh (Locality 1), but in places is gradational or even laterally interfingering (Locality 10).

Route from Kyle of Lochalsh

Drive east along the A87 for about 6 miles, then the A890 to Strathcarron. After crossing the River Carron turn left along the A896 to Loch Kishorn (all mostly Moine and Lewisian terrain). A dramatic change in the scenery coincides with the passage into uninterrupted Torridonian sandstone country, north of Loch Kishorn, with the cirque cliffs of Beinn Bhan (895m) on the left being characteristic of the Applecross Formation. Beyond lies the coastal village of Shieldaig, and a short distance on is Ob Mheallaidh, an almost enclosed embayment of Loch Torridon, the first stop of this itinerary.

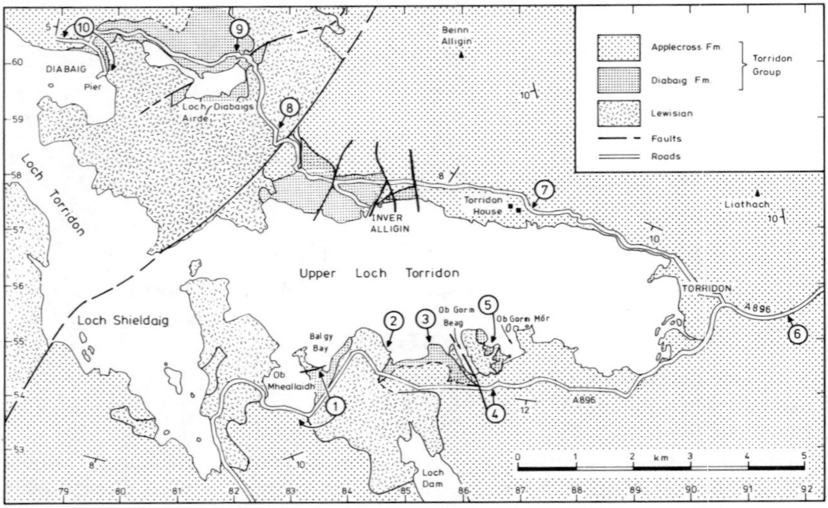

Figure 39. Geological and locality map of the Loch Torridon area. Itinerary IX.

If time is limited on this itinerary, it is recommended that visitors focus on Localities 1, 9 and 10.

Localities 1-6 provide a comprehensive view of the range of lithologies and facies relationships along the southern side of Loch Torridon. Localities 8-10 together provide a view of the entire lower part of the Torridon Group on the northern side of the loch. Relatively low tides are preferable at Localities 2, 5 and 10. All localities are in Figure 39.

Locality 1 (NG 830537). Diabaig Formation, Ob Mheallaidh (1 hour). Along the southern shore of Ob Mheallaidh the sediments of the Diabaig Formation occupy an valley between two basement hills. Almost horizontal shaly beds with ripple-marked bedding surfaces and desiccation cracks are exposed on the shore. Along the road there is a splendid section through ripple-bedded sandstones with gneiss pebbles, and siltstones. These beds are seen again in the southeastern corner of Ob Mheallaidh, by the roadside, in contact with gneiss (NG 83385364). The contact between the Diabaig and Applecross formations is not exposed above the road, but may be examined on the peninsula jutting out to the north-east of Ob Mheallaidh. On the north coast of this peninsula the erosive contact can be seen in a small wooded bluff (NG 834545). It is almost horizontal and may be traced northwestwards along the coast at low tide.

Locality 2 (NG 846543). Diabaig Formation, West Balgy Bay (30 minutes). Exposures above high water mark, on the west side of Balgy Bay about 600m north of the road bridge show interbedded gneiss cobble conglomerate and grey sandstone dipping off the gneiss ridge. Basic gneiss clasts are an important component in the conglomerate. They are derived from basic dykes exposed nearby in the basement and demonstrate the very limited transport typical of Diabaig sediment.

Locality 3 (NG 846543). Diabaig Formation, east Balgy Bay (30 minutes). Here, extensive exposures of almost horizontally bedded rippled, greenish grey sandstones occur along the shore. East of grid line 854 the ripple facies is conformably underlain by red sandstones with planar cross-lamination in sets 1-3m thick. They are quite atypical of the formation. In the small bay at (NG 857548) they pass downwards into breccias overlying basement gneiss.

Locality 4 (NG 865542). Torridon Group and Lewisian gneiss south of Ob Gorm Beag (30 minutes). A road cutting 300m south of Ob Gorm Beag and 300m west of the car park (NG 862541) shows gneiss breccia overlain by Diabaig and Applecross sediments. The Diabaig Formation is about 10m thick, the lower parts composed of gneiss breccia and the rest of ripple-topped sandstone beds with intercalations of red shale. These sediments have been faulted up about 80m from their lateral equivalents on the shore of Ob Gorm Mor. The fault responsible forms the western margin of Ob Gorm Beag and cuts the eastern edge of the roadside outcrop.

Locality 5 (NG 865542). Torridon Group, west Ob Gorm Mor (30 minutes). The Diabaig Formation includes gneiss breccia, particularly well seen in the southern part of the bay, and flaggy ripple-marked sandstones. The Applecross sandstone facies overlies the Diabaig Formation at several points. It is extensively exposed at the north end of Ard Mhor (NG 863552).

Contacts between the Diabaig Formation and the irregular gneiss topography are well seen in this bay.

Locality 6 (NG 917556). Applecross Formation, Torridon Village (15 minutes). Pebbly red sandstones of the Applecross Formation occur near the road about 2km east of Torridon village (NG 917556). This facies is typical of the Applecross Formation further north. Pebbles reach 3-4cm in size and include all the usual types.

Locality 7 (NG 879572). Applecross Formation, Torridon House (30 minutes). Roadside exposures here show the top of an alluvial fan in the lower part of the Applecross Formation (NG 879572).

Locality 8 Lewisian-Torridon Group unconformity (15 minutes). About a kilometre south along the road from Locality 9, at NG 827587, there is a splendid view of the pre-Torridon Group topography along the southern side of Upper Loch Torridon. Silvery grey gneiss can be clearly seen below the almost horizontally bedded sandstones of the Applecross Formation. The extent to which the present relief, particularly at Ob Mheallaidh, coincides with pre-Torridonian relief can be easily seen.

Locality 9 (NG 821601). Diabaig Formation, Loch Diabaig's Airde (1 hour). The lower part of the Diabaig Formation and underlying gneiss are well exposed along the road near the northeast corner of the loch. The succession is duplicated by a fault. Stop at the bend in the road at NG 82146008 west of the fault. Basal breccia is well exposed by the roadside, only half a metre from gneiss. To the west, discontinuous roadside exposures display an upward-fining stratigraphic sequence. The highest beds, about 350m along the road at NG 81886008, are red and grey ripple-laminated siltstones. To the northeast the up-dip equivalents of these fine-grained deposits can be seen above the recent screes, with basement gneiss beyond. These laterally equivalent beds are flaggy red sandstones and gneiss breccias containing clasts up to 10cm or more.

East of the fault, breccia and basement gneiss are again seen by the roadside at NG 82376000 but the actual contact is concealed by a stream. Stratigraphically above, to the north-west, are thick-bedded purplish sandstones with gneiss clasts. The sandstones show evidence of pre-Pleistocene weathering – the crumbly nature of the outcrop at this point is quite unusual in such sandstones. The highest beds seen in this section are about 150m along the road from the unconformity.

These deposits are thought to result from lateral equivalence of basement hills, fanglomerates and lake or shallow marine deposits (these are best seen in the Diabiag shore section (Locality 10).

Locality 10 (NG 797598). Diabaig to Applecross Formations, Diabaig (2-3 hours). The Diabaig Formation is well exposed along the shore north of the jetty at Diabaig (NG 797598) (Fig. 40a). The jetty is built on a promontory of gneiss, fringed on its north-west side by a small outcrop of basal gneiss conglomerate (Fig. 40b).

The section proper starts at NG 79736013 where coarse grey sandstone with gneiss fragments up to 10cm is exposed beneath some trees between high water mark and the road. About 20m north-west, gneiss debris does not exceed a centimetre in size. Beyond this point the strata are predominantly grey shales with occasional thin grey sandstones ripple-laminated and frequently convoluted (Fig. 40c). Desiccation polygons and ripples are common in the shales and rare synaeresis cracks are present. At NG 79406024, about 75m stratigraphically above the base of the sequence, a half-metre sandstone bed with gneiss fragments up to 0.7cm appears. Beyond this point grey sandstone beds are common. They frequently show signs of grading and ripple laminated tops, but lateral persistency is low.

From their petrography and stratigraphic setting these grey sandstones are very likely turbidites generated by the Applecross river system. In this area the Diabiag and Applecross formations were evidently contemporaneous facies.

The Diabaig sediments from boron-in-illite studies were probably lacustrine (Stewart & Parker, 1979) but the cryptarchs (Peat & Diver, 1982) in the abundant phosphatic laminae and pods suggest a marine connection (Will Diver, pers. comm.).

The top of the Diabaig Formation is drawn at a coarse pink sandstone with trough cross-bedding exposed in the wood just above high water mark about 30m east of Allt na Beiste (NG 79306026).

Higher strata are assigned to the Applecross Formation. They are coarse grained and red, though not pebbly for the first 40m. The upper part of this fine-grained member contains red and grey siltstones. The member is interpreted as an

Figure 40. The Diabaig Formation at its type locality, Itinerary IX, Locality 10. (a) Shore section at Diabaig. In the foreground are gently dipping shales. The hills in the background are of Lewisian basement. Diabaig jetty (for location of (b) is in the right background. (b) Contact between the Lewisian gneiss and basal conglomerates of the Diabaig Formation, Diabaig jetty. (c) Wave ripples on shale bedding surfaces in shore section. (d) Large-scale contorted bedding in the overlying Applecross Formation, above sea cliffs, west end of shore section.

alluvial fan inter-fingering with Diabaig Formation lake sediment. Due to faulting and the low dip, the top of the Diabaig continues to outcrop just above high water mark for a further 300m along the shore. About 50m beyond the township wall (NG 78836028) grey shales in the lowest member of the Applecross Formation are well exposed on the low cliff a few metres above high water mark. Some 10m higher in the section, an erosion surface followed by coarse pebbly sandstone marks the base of the next alluvial fan in the Applecross Formation. About 200m west of the wall, 45m about sea level, there are two very large exposures (NG 78636038) and (NG 76676037) of pebbly Applecross sandstones which show a wide range of soft sediment contortions (Fig. 40). Average grain size is in the range 0.2-1mm. Structures include overturned foresets, isolated cusps, cusp trains, cusp erosion by the following bed, and cusps affecting more than one cross-bedded set. The lower of the two exposures shows extensive sheets of sandstone with recumbent folds overturned in the palaeocurrent direction, perhaps due to slumping.

About 350m northeast of these outcrops the Craig–Diabaig path can be reached, near where it joins the townland and the road back to Diabaig jetty.

Route to Gairloch

Leaving Diabaig return to A896 and continue through Glen Torridon. On the left Liathach rises to 1054m, made up principally of near horizontal Applecross Formation sandstones, but with a cap of Cambrian quartzite on its eastern and highest summit. Further on, also on the left, rises Beinn Eighe (1010m), composed largely of Cambrian quartzite, thus demonstrating the inclined nature of the Torridonian-Cambrian unconformity, and indicating that the Torridonian rocks were tilted after deposition, then subsequently tilted back to near-horizontal after the Cambrian strata were deposited.

The road enters the Beinn Eighe Nature Reserve, which includes a protected remnant of the ancient Caledonian pine forest, noted for its flora and fauna. At Kinlochewe, take the A832 to the north-west towards Gairloch. The road passes alongside fault-controlled Loch Maree. The loch is dominated by Slioch (960m) a mountain of Applecross Formation sandstones, resting on Lewisian basement which hereabouts also illustrates the hilly nature of the basement on which the Torridonian was built (cover photograph).

The Lewisian between here and Gairloch comprises metasedimentary schists intercalated with amphibolites which form the Loch Maree Group. This group forms two belts 5km and 2km wide at Loch Maree and Gairloch respectively, within the Laxfordian gneisses. It has been suggested that the Gairloch metasediments are around 2200Ma, so it seems likely that the Loch Maree Group represents the only surviving relic of an Early Proterozoic supracrustal succession, laid down unconformably on the Archaean basement, and then deformed and metamorphosed during the Laxfordian. (These rocks are described in Barber *et al.*, 1978 Itinerary VI).

ITINERARY X

Stoer Group and Aultbea Formation (Torridonian), Gruinard Bay.

A. D. STEWART

Maps: Geological Survey Sheet 92
Ordnance Survey 1:50,000 Sheet 19

Gruinard Bay provides a good coastal section through the lower part of the Stoer Group. There are also good coastal exposures of the Aultbea Formation, which are characterised by spectacular contortions in sandstones. The district also shows the irregular nature of the Lewisian basement with good examples of pre-Stoer Group palaeovalleys exhumed in Palaeozoic time. These localities are shown in Figure 41.

Route

From Gairloch follow the A832 to Laide, then take the minor road north along the west coast of Gruinard Bay to Mellon Udrigle. Parking is available close to the sandy beach of Camas a'Charraig, from which fine views of the Torridonian mountains of Ben More Coigach and An Teallach rising above Lewisian basement may be had on a clear day.

Locality 1 (NG 890960). Aultbea Formation, Creag an Eilein, north of Mellon Udrigle (2 hours). From the car park in Mellon Udrigle take the track leading northwest then north to its end (1.5km). Along the rocky coast southwest of the point of Creag an Eilein are excellent exposures of Aultbea Formation sandstones (NG 887976). The sandstones are typically trough cross-bedded and rippled, probably representing migrating fluvial channels with overbank deposits. Much of the formation at this locality has been subjected to soft-sediment deformation, as indicated by complex contortions of bedded and trough cross-stratified units (Fig. 42a). Earthquake shocks have been invoked to explain these contortions, but it is also possible that rapid loading of soft, water-saturated, sediment may also have resulted in liquefaction.

Return to Mellon Udrigle by the same route and proceed back to Laide. Then continue east along the A832 for 2.5km, parking by the roadside just east of First Coast. Locality 2 is about 200m from the road.

Locality 2 (NG 926911). Stoer Group, First Coast and Second Coast (2-3 hours). A narrow inlet with a shingle beach at its head (NG 92609110) marks the stratigraphic top of a section 150m thick. Immediately to the west the succession

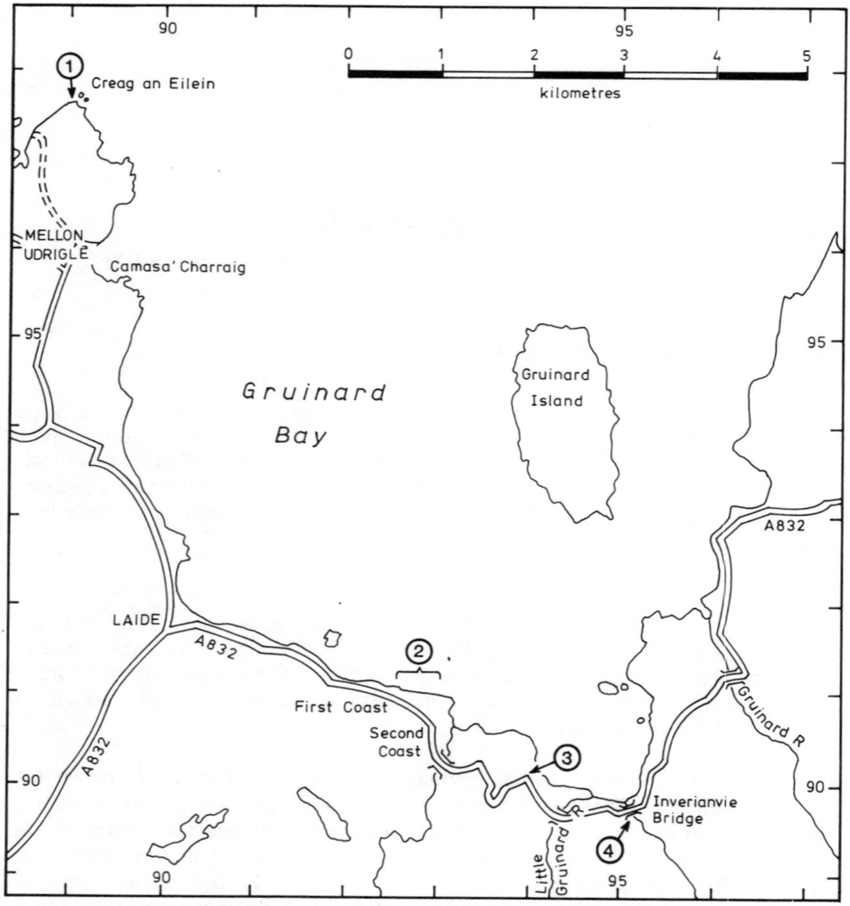

Figure 41. Map showing Itinerary X localities in the Gruinard Bay district.

is truncated by a fault, but for 250m along the rocky coast to the east the Stoer Group is perfectly exposed (Fig. 43). The base, at NG 92959103, rests on gneiss. A volcanic sandstone with gneiss pebbles and cobbles, and glassy shards, known as Stac Fada Member from its type locality at Stoer, occurs about 25m below the top. This is a distinctive and widespread marker horizon in the Stoer Group and is believed to represent outwash from local gneissic basement hills heavily contaminated by air-fall tuff. (Fig. 42b). It is underlain by trough cross-bedded red sandstones with exotic pebbles of fluvial origin. The base of these sandstones is sharp and marked by a flood of roughly aligned elliptical pebbles, and a steep cliff 4m high. Beneath come ripple-marked and desiccated red shales and

Figure 42. Facies in the Aultbea Formation and Stoer Group in the Gruinard Bay district, Itinerary X. (a) Contorted bedding in the Aultbea Formation, Creag an Eilein north of Mellon Udrigle in the northwest part of the bay (Locality 1). (b) Stoer Group, south shore of Gruinard Bay near Second Coast, Locality 2 showing the Stac Fada Member, a volcanic debris-flow with gneiss fragments. (c) Stoer Group red shales and sandstones of a temporary lake succession, Locality 2. (d) Basal conglomerate of the Stoer Group, Inverianvie Bridge, Locality 5. The bridge can be seen at the head of the bay in the Frontispiece, and the conglomerate occurs in the valley immediately to the right of the bridge.

sandstones with angular gneiss debris (Fig. 42c), formed mainly in a playa lake. The steep cliff can be quite easily descended without a rope, at a point where it is intersected by a small fault, to reach a large rippled bedding surface. The shaly sequence, which is about 30m thick, is deeply dissected by the sea and can only be completely traversed at low tide. Below come more easily accessible flaggy red sandstones with gneiss debris which increase in abundance towards the base of the section. The size of the gneiss fragments also increases down-section, reaching

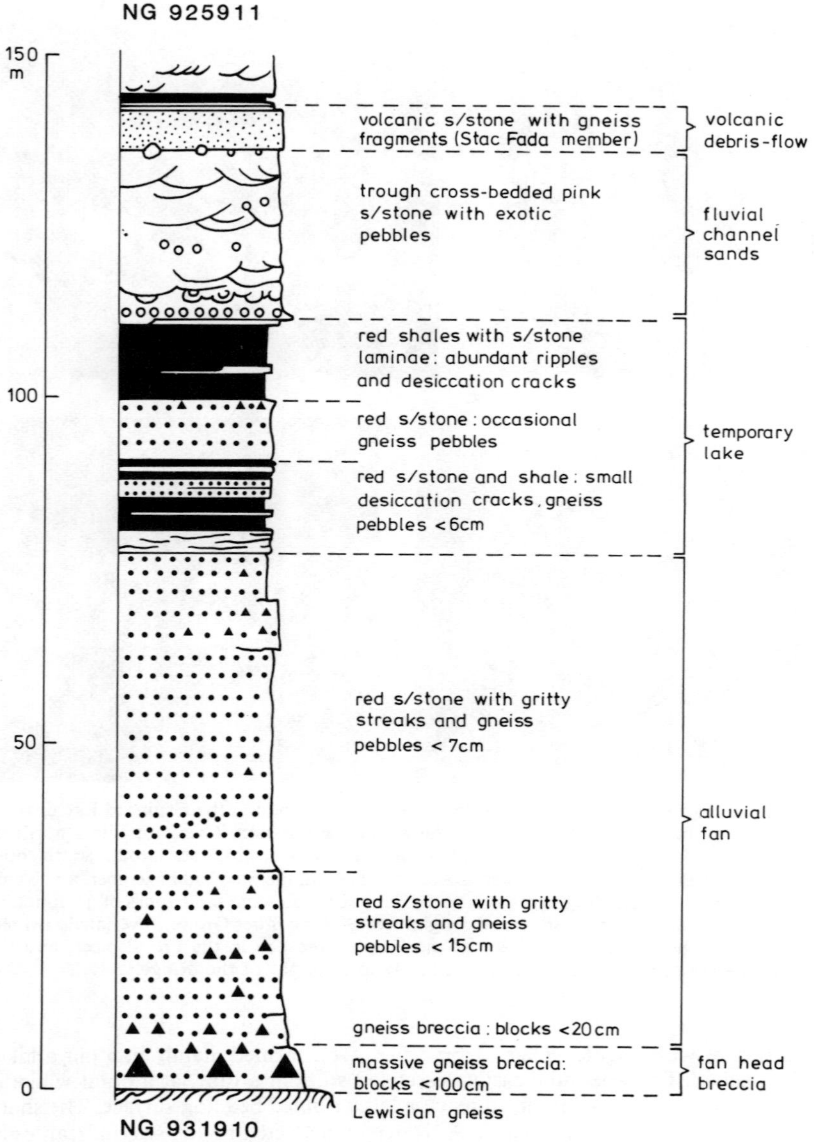

Figure 43. Graphic log and environmental interpretation of the Stoer Group on the shore near Second Coast, Gruinard Bay, Itinerary X, Locality 2 (from Stewart 1978, Fig. 16).

1m or more within a few metres of the base. Boulders are predominantly subrounded to subangular, and were probably deposited near the head of an alluvial fan during flash floods.

Locality 3 (NG 94039013). Stoer Group unconformity, Little Gruinard viewpoint (15 minutes). Stop at the small car park on the left side of the road just beyond the crest of the hill. Even better views are obtainable from the small hill above the car park (Frontispiece). To the north one looks along the trace of the basal Stoer Group unconformity. Most of the gneiss topography along this line has been exhumed from beneath the Stoer Group, in particular the headlands of Gruinard Bay (including that at the observation point), Carn Dearg an Droma, Scoraig, Horse Island and Rubha Dunan (Achiltibuie). This is one of the oldest landscapes in the world. Note the position of Inverianvie Bridge for Locality 4. In the distance, rising above the Lewisian basement is An Teallach made up of Applecross sandstones.

Locality 4 (NG 951898). Basal Stoer Group, Inverianvie Bridge (30 minutes). On the west side of the river, about 20m upstream from the bridge, the basal conglomerate of the Stoer Group is well exposed on a small cliff (Fig. 42d). It contains perfectly elliptical gneiss boulders up to 2m across. Some 50m of conglomerate, stratigraphically higher than that on this cliff can be seen in the nearby road cut. Clast size, abundance, and degree of rounding diminish upwards and a crude tabular bedding appears. The high degree of roundness suggests high energy fluvial environments, like those of the Reinachait Member at Stoer (Itinerary XII, locs. 4 and 5c).

Route to Ullapool

From Gruinard Bay the A832 is followed through Torridonian country alongside Little Loch Broom and the Dundonnell River, then over high moorland to the gorge of the River Broom, crossing the Moine Thrust zone into the Moine Assemblage. From there the A835 is taken to Ullapool alongside Loch Broom, recrossing the Moine Thrust, back into Torridonian terrain.

ITINERARY XI

Stoer and Torridon Groups, Enard Bay and Achiltibuie

A. D. STEWART

Maps: Geological Survey 1:50,000 Survey Sheet 101
Ordnance Survey 1:50,000, Sheet 15

The relationships between the Stoer and Torridon Groups are conveniently studied in the area of Enard Bay and Achiltibuie (Fig. 44). In the Enard Bay exposures (Fig. 45 a & b), described in detail by Gracie & Stewart (1967), the Stac Fada Member and a distinctive limestone of the Stoer type section are seen unconformably overlain by the Diabaig and Applecross formations of the Torridon Group. The exposures are best seen at low tide. At Achiltibuie (Fig. 46) the sandstone conglomerates of the Torridon Group, which overlie the unconformity, were originally assigned by the Geological Survey to the Triassic system. In 1953, however, Irving detected a major palaeomagnetic break in the Torridonian in this area (Irving & Runcorn, 1957), later interpreted as an unconformity by Stewart (1966a) and shown to coincide precisely with the unconformity at Locality 2C (Stewart & Irving, 1974). The same magnetic break also occurs at Enard Bay between sample sites corresponding to Localities D and F of the itinerary below. The exposures near Achiltibuie can be seen at most stages of the tide.

If desired, the rather monotonous Aultbea Formation may be conveniently examined along the coast northwest of Achiltibuie. Details are given under Locality 4 (Fig. 44).

Route

From Ullapool follow the A835 northwards to Drumrunie, and then the single track road to the WNW. The Applecross Formation peaks of Cul Beag (769m) and Stac Pollaidh (603m) are prominent on the right.

Locality 1 (starting at NC 025127). Unconformities between Lewisian Gneiss, Stoer Group and the Torridon Group, Enard Bay, (3-4 hours). Leave the road near the bend at (NC 025127), about 4km north of Achiltibuie, and follow the coast northward. There is no path but the ground is not difficult. At NC 022131 a small knob of rock not far from high water mark contains the typical exotic pebble suite of the Stoer Group. This is the highest stratigraphic level seen in this area and the only one with this pebble suite. Continuing northwards along the coast, fine exposures of red sandstone are found.

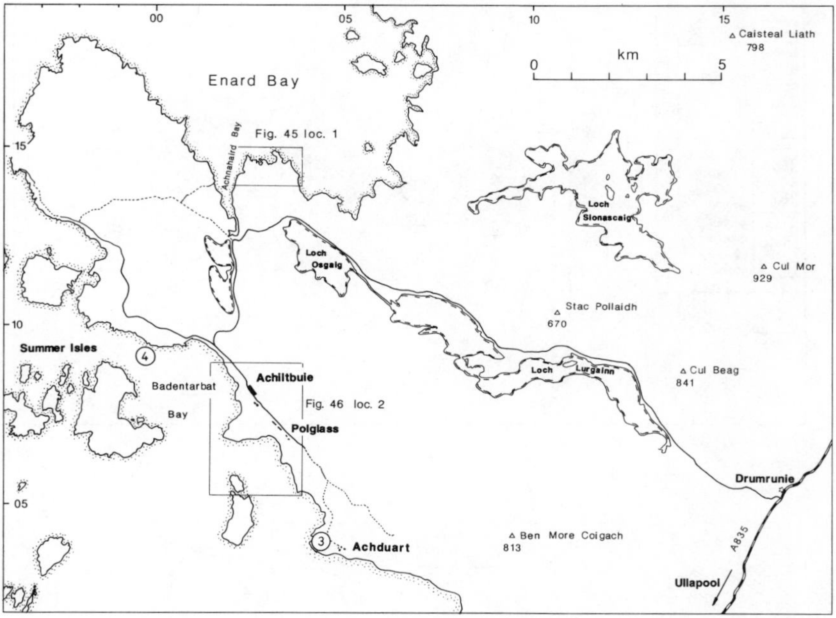

Figure 44. Map showing Itinerary XI localities in the Enard Bay-Achiltibuie district.

1A. Red sandstones with cross bedding in tabular sets up to 2m thick can be studied in three dimensions along the coast at A (Unit III) in Figure 45a. This is the Rudha Beag Sandstone of Gracie & Stewart (1967). The sandstones correlate with those of Stoer (Itinerary XII, Locality 3) and have a similar origin.
1B. Descend the Rudha Beag Sandstone scarp by the sheep path to high water mark. The sandstone rests abruptly on red mudstone with an erosive contact. A few metres to the east, across the little bay, the red mudstones pass laterally into angular gneiss breccia which in turn mantles a gneiss hill. Limestone partly cements the breccia.
1C. Cross the gneiss hill to the bay with the ruined bothy, noticing on the way the lateral equivalence of Stoer Group breccia and flaggy red sandstones. About 100m NNE of the bothy the gneiss breccia of the Stoer Group is covered by limestone, possibly algal, similar to that at Stoer, overlain in turn by red mudstone (C on Fig. 45a). A thick deposit of sandstone boulder conglomerate overlies the red mudstone here. The mudstone has been picked out by the sea to form a gully. **Do not hammer the limestone.**
1D. Follow the southern edge of the sandstone boulder conglomerate outcrop to the next bay (D in Fig. 45a). Here the conglomerate again overlies red mudstone which has a well-developed limestone band within it **(do not hammer)**. There is no basal breccia here – the mudstone instead passes down into the winnowed top of the volcanogenic Stac Fada Member. This winnowed top is several metres thick

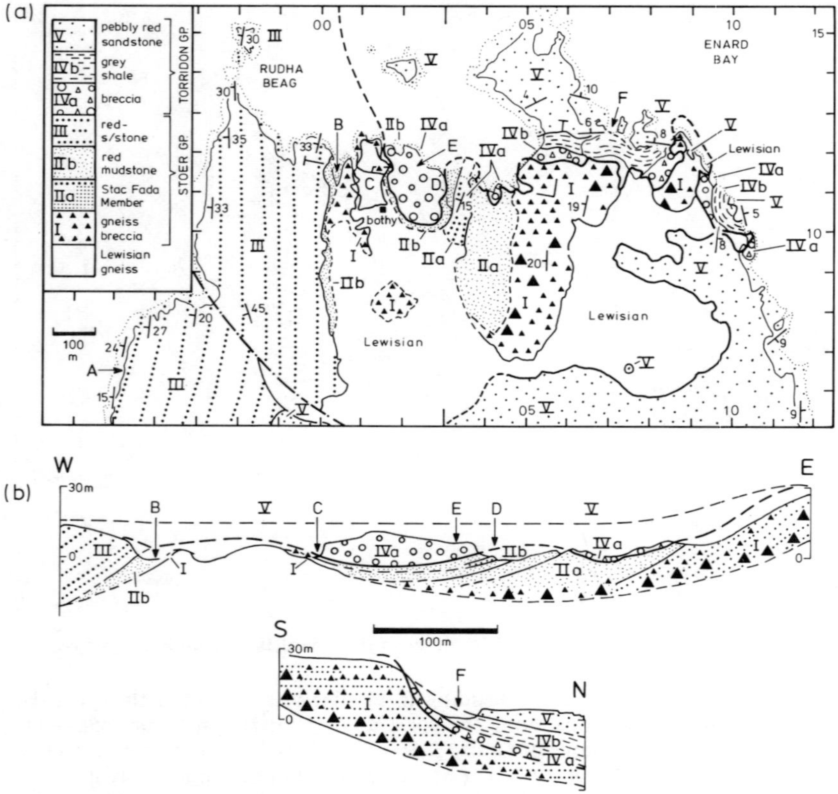

Figure 45. (a) Geological map and (b) sections through the Stoer and Torridon groups on the southern shore of Enard Bay, Itinerary XI, Locality 1 (modified after Gracie & Stewart, 1967 and Stewart 1978, Figs. 13 & 14).

and replete with small scours and impersistent graded beds. Beneath comes the massive part of the Stac Fada Member (structureless sandstone facies of Gracie & Stewart, 1967), the upper part of which is packed with pea-sized accretionary lapilli. In places the member is veneered by a breccia composed exclusively of Stac Fada material – the basal breccia of the Torridon Group.

1E. The sandstone boulder conglomerate is seen at (E in Figure 45a). This is made up exclusively of blocks derived from the Rudha Beag Sandstone, some as much as 10m across. The sandstone originally overlay red mudstone here, as it does to the west, and may have formed an unstable cliff which periodically collapsed or slipped (cf. Anderson & Dunham, 1966, Fig. 22).

1F. An almost enclosed bay at F in Figure 45a has been eroded in typical grey shales of the Diabaig Formation. The basal breccia beneath, laterally equivalent to the shales, is here made up of gneiss debris, thus tending to reflect as usual the composition of the rocks it unconformably overlies. In fact the Stoer Group at this point is also composed of gneiss breccia, carved into the form of a cliff partially smothered by younger breccias of the Diabaig Formation. Hay *et al.* (1988) have recorded both detrital and diagenetic pumpellyite in the Stoer breccias here. The resulting green colours are easily visible in outcrop. On the coast 200m to the west, the grey Diabaig shales show interesting channels several metres across of possible inter-tidal origin. The shales are overlain sharply by the coarse, pebbly red sandstones of the Applecross Formation.

From here it is more convenient to follow the coast SSE to the road bridge (NC 039130), rather than walk straight back to the starting point at NC 025127 across soggy peat hags.

Locality 2 (NC 023086). Unconformities between the Lewisian gneiss, Stoer Group and Torridon Group, Achiltbuie (2-3 hours).

2A. The Stac Fada Member is seen on the coast west of the Summer Isles Hotel at Achiltibuie (NC 022082, A in Fig. 46). The member is here only 2m thick, rests on gneiss and is overlain by 3m of fine red sandstone and siltstone. The section is covered at high water. Follow the coast south across the gneiss, sandstone conglomerate and a shingle beach underlain by flaggy red sandstone and grey shale of the Diabaig Formation. The grey shale is only visible at low tide.

2B. At the south end of the shingle beach the basal conglomerate of the Diabaig Formation is again seen at B in Figure 46. Unlike that at the northern end of the shingle beach, it is composed mainly of gneiss fragments with relatively little sandstone and a few fragments from the Stac Fada Member.

2C. The Stoer/Torridon Group unconformity is perfectly exposed on a sea cliff at C in Figure 46, apparently dipping steeply eastward. To the east the cliff degenerates into a beach bar, although there are exposures near high water mark. These exposures are of gently dipping red Diabaig strata containing blocks of red sandstone up to 4m across, indistinguishable in their sedimentary structures and petrography from those of the Stoer Group beneath the unconformity. The red Diabaig Formation becomes shaly upwards and eventually grey; however the exposures are discontinuous and only exposed at low tide. Below the unconformity, to the west, the Stoer Group dips about 30° westwards. The red sandstones contain gneiss pebbles and chips, but no sandstone clasts. The sandstones are predominantly flaggy but contain occasional small channels.

2D. Follow the present cliff-line westwards for 300m (possible at low tide) to a fault at NC 02260675, D in Figure 46. Patches of flaggy red sandstone and sandstone conglomerate of the Diabiag Formation adhere to the cliff which evidently existed in Diabiag times. West of the fault the Diabaig is not seen again. The cliffs are made of Stoer Group red sandstones, which continue to dip west until they abut the top of an ancient gneiss hill, exhumed at the western tip of the peninsula, and in two small tidal islets.

2E. From the unconformity at Locality 2C follow the coast to the east and south crossing Diabaig grey shales and Applecross red sandstones. At E in Figure 46 some 10m of the grey shales are exposed. Desiccation cracks and ripple lamination are common. The shales are sharply bounded above by typical pebbly Applecross sandstones. Grey sandstone units up to 0.5m thick, are present in the topmost Diabaig Formation. Some show graded bedding and have rippled tops.

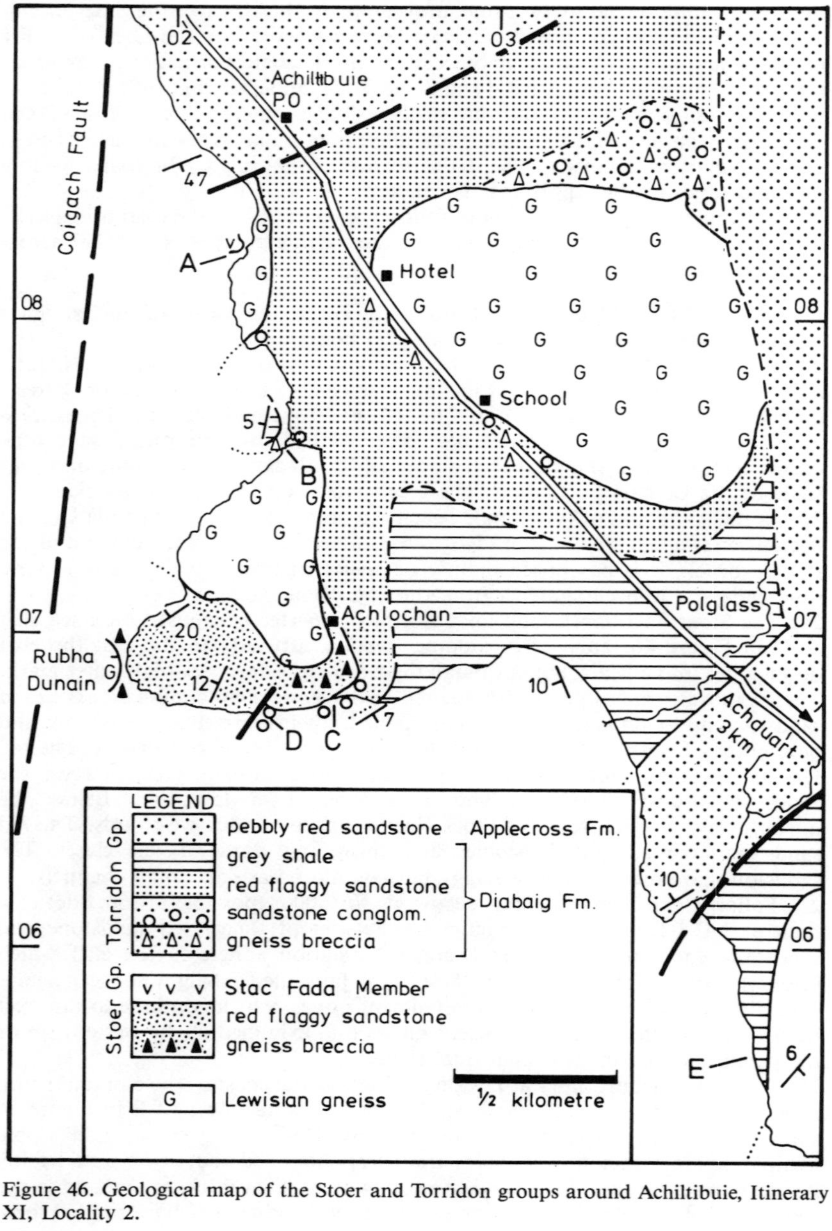

Figure 46. Geological map of the Stoer and Torridon groups around Achiltibuie, Itinerary XI, Locality 2.

They can also be seen at Diabaig (Itinerary IX, Locality 10) and have been described from the same stratigraphic level in Raasay (Selley, 1965, Figs. 10 and 12).

Locality 3 (NC 046040). Relationship between Applecross & Diabaig Formations, Achduart (1 hour). Follow the road which leads south to Achduart. Stop at the summit NC 046040 and walk SW across country for about 0.5km to a cairn on the cliff top NC 04270380. Just south of the cairn, above high-water mark, is the base of the Applecross Formation, erosive on reddened Diabaig shales. From here eastwards for about 300m the coast exposes a 40m thick fining-upward sequence in the Applecross Formation. This is almost certainly an alluvial fan, similar to that described by Williams (1969b) near Cape Wrath, but much thinner. The fine-grained top at NC 04490355 is sharply overlain by very coarse, pebbly sandstones, with palaeocurrents flowing SE as compared with northeast in the unit beneath. The pebbly sandstones also fine upwards, this time over 130m stratigraphically. The top is exposed on the coast southeast of Achduart NC 05260347. The lower of these two members can be mapped towards the NE for 15km into Inverpolly Forest, thickening all the while. To the south it thins and cannot be traced beyond the Scoraig peninsula, about 7km from Achduart. The upper member can be mapped south for at least 20km, into Fisherfield Forest.

Locality 4 (NC 008096). Aultbea Formation, northwest of Achiltibuie (2-3 hours). A complete section through the Aultbea Formation is exposed in low, easily accessible cliffs along the coast north-west of Achiltibuie. The section is 6km long and the stratigraphic thickness is 1.2km. The rocks are rather monotonous medium-grained, highly contorted red sandstones. An intercalated unit of ripple-laminated fine sandstone and siltstone, now mainly red but probably originally grey, occurs on the coast about 200m south of Dornie NB 986100. The unit is about 3.6m thick, bounded by major erosion surfaces. This horizon, or one stratigraphically very close to it, crops out nearby in the Summer Isles, where it has yielded cryptarchs (Zhang *et al.*, 1981; Zhang, 1982). It is also found at intervals for 70km to the south, e.g. at Mellon Charles NG 845908, Torridon NG 935578, and in Applecross Forest (NG 770431), always very close to the Applecross–Aultbea boundary. Time correlation is established by its coincidence with a zone of rapid palaeomagnetic polarity reversals, both here, and at Torridon and Toscaig (Smith *et al.*, 1983). The base of the Aultbea Formation in this section, marked by the abrupt disappearance of the typical Applecross pebble suite, is seen on the coast at NB 980104. The highest beds crop out about 150m north-east of the old pier, at NC 009095. The formation must be overlain by the basal Cambrian quartzite (seen on the coast northwest of Achiltibuie) but the contact is not exposed. The whole sequence is juxtaposed with basal beds of the Torridon Group at Achiltibuie by the intervention of the Coigach fault. The fault cuts the coast about a kilometre east of the pier.

Route to Lochinver

Return to Drumrunie on the A835, turning northeast to Ledmore. Thence follow the A837 to Lochinver. The road follows roughly the line of the Moine Thrust.

Figure 47. Lochinver: irregular Lewisian basement with Suilven (789m) comprising Applecross Formation sandstones rising above.

To the west lies Lewisian basement with isolated Torridonian sandstone peaks (Fig. 47), to the east of the Moine Assemblage. Adjacent to the thrust Cambro-Ordovician carbonates and quartzites have been caught up with the older rocks in complex imbricate or duplex structures.

En route to Lochinver, along the north shore of Loch Assynt an additional stop may be made to examine basal Torridon Group sediments.

Locality 5 (NC 21282519). Basal Torridon Group, Loch Assynt (30 minutes). On the north shore of Loch Assynt (north of map Fig. 44) a small cutting is renowned as the locality which yielded Dreikanter to the Geological Survey (Selley, 1966, p. 296-98). The beds are dark reddish-grey tabular sandstones with gneiss debris. Similar beds are well exposed to the east, along the roadside. About 400m east of the small cutting Lewisian appears beneath the sandstones and can be followed for over 200m, as far as NC 218250. The unconformity is perfectly exposed. Both Lewisian and overlying sandstone show deep weathering, evidently post-dating the deposition of the Torridon Group and probably of pre-Pleistocene age. These tabular beds with Lewisian detritus probably belong to the Diabaig formation. Typical Applecross sandstones with exotic pebbles overlie them and appear by the road to the east.

ITINERARY XII

Stoer Group (Torridonian) Stoer Peninsula

A. D. STEWART

Maps: Geological Survey 1:50,000 Sheet 107
Ordnance Survey 1:50,000 Sheet 15.

The main features of the Stoer Group can be seen in a long day based either at Lochinver or Stoer. For the first part of the Itinery, it is best to examine the type section of the Stoer Group (Fig. 48) (Localities 2 and 3) which starts at the basal unconformity by the old cemetery at Stoer (NC 041284) and continues westwards along the north side of Stoer Bay to Rubha'a'Mhill Dheirg. The coastal part of the traverse, particularly that near Locality 3C, is best seen at low tide, Next, strata laterally equivalent to the type section but about a kilometre to the south, at Clachtoll, repay a visit (Locality 1). North of Stoer village, the conglomerate facies is well seen at Reinachait (Locality 4). Lastly, the north coast of the Stoer peninsula (Localities 5A–F) displays a fine section through the lower part of the Group, quite different, however, from the stratigraphically equivalent part of the type section. The north coast strata are unconformably overlain at Locality 5F by the Diabaig and Applecross Formations of the Torridon Group. The Diabaig Formation can only be seen properly at low tide.

Locality 1 (NC 042272) Basal conglomerate of the Stoer Group, Clachtoll (1½ hours).

1A. Gneiss conglomerate overlies unweathered Lewisian basement all the way from the type section, at Stoer Cemetery, southwards. The best exposure (Loc. 1A, Fig. 48) (NC 043273) is 1.2km south of Stoer cemetery and about 150m east of the main road. The lowest 10m of the conglomerate is massive and consists of tightly packed decimetre-sized gneiss cobbles, some of which are quite well rounded. Ten metres above the base a crude tubular bedding appears, pebble size diminishes and finally the deposit passes upwards into a dark red muddy sandstone. This can be seen in a small quarry by the roadside (NC 04222728).
1B. West of the road the coastal exposures show several features of the lower part of the Stoer Group which complement those seen in the type section (Localities 2 and 3). For example, limestones are best seen in the muddy sandstones east of the great cleft rock A'Chlach Thuill **(do not hammer them)**. They crop out on both coasts of the peninsula of Locality 1B (Fig. 48). The limestones show desiccation cracks, partially healed by subsequent accretion of limestone, and other features suggesting shallow water algal growth.

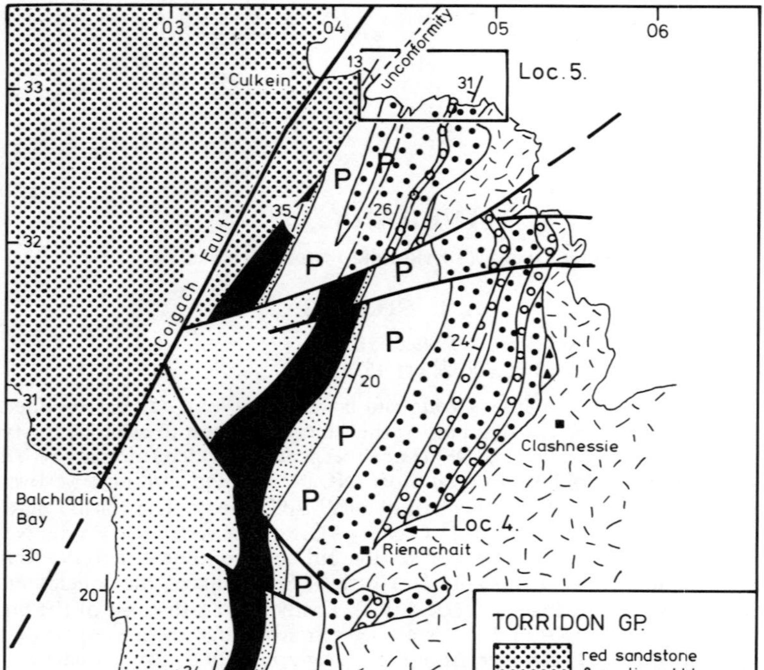

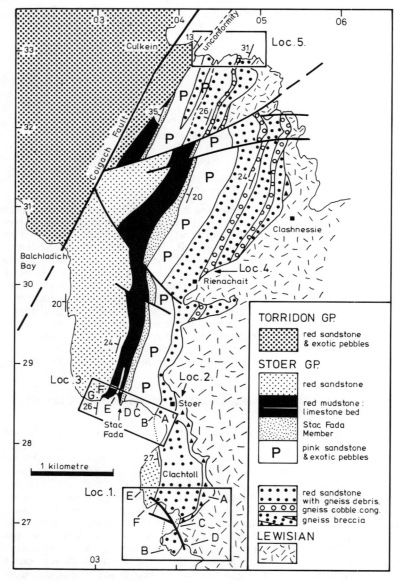

Figure 48. Geological map of the Stoer and Torridon groups in the Stoer peninsula, Itinerary XII. For a more detailed map of Locality 5 see Figure 51 (from Stewart 1975, Fig. 7).

1C. Here, at NC 04022704 (Fig. 48), massive muddy sandstone, dark red in colour, passes laterally into a centimetre-laminated variety which in turn becomes gritty and passes into gneiss breccia next to the basement gneiss. This lateral facies change, as the gneiss is approached, takes place over 10m.

The breccio-conglomerates overlying the basement are fanglomerates which fine upwards due to fan-head retreat. The toes of the fanglomerates extended into temporary lakes, now represented by the muddy sandstone. The evidence of repeated desiccation in the muddy sandstones (seen on sand-scoured surfaces) suggests the original presence of smectitic clays which expanded and contracted with seasonal wetting, destroying the banding which this facies almost certainly had when it was first deposited. There appears to have been no through drainage in palaeovalleys containing the muddy sandstone facies, unlike the palaeovalley north of Stoer which contains cross-bedded sandstones and cobble conglomerates.

1D. The base of the Stoer Group may be seen at low-tide if the sand level is low on the east side of the small bay at Locality 1D. (Fig. 48) (NC 040267). There is little breccia here. Muddy sandstone injects the underlying gneiss which shows extensive *in-situ* fracturing on the southward facing cliff. This perhaps resulted from the high pore-water pressures in the overlying sediment, the result of seismic action. By contrast the conspicuous tongue of breccia 50m to the south at high water mark is quite similar to the basal facies elsewhere. The local derivation of the material is evident from its content of picrite debris and vein quartz, both from the subjacent gneiss only a few metres distant.

1E. The three couplets of muddy red sandstone–rippled red sandstone and siltstone, intercalated in the trough-cross bedded red sandstones at Locality 3C are also splendidly exposed on the coast of Clachtoll at Locality 1E in Figure 48 (NC 035273). They may be seen at any stage of the tide. The cupriferous nodules in the upper part of one of these couplets have been described by Fermor (1951).

IF. Slump rolls on the north side of the Bay of Clachtoll (NC 037272), well exposed near high water mark (Locality 1F in Fig, 48), indicate a palaeoslope towards the northwest. This contrasts with the palaeocurrent directions in the Stoer Group below this level, generally to the west, and above this level, which are generally to the east. A similar reversal of palaeocurrent direction occurs at the level of the Stac Fada Member at Locality 3.

Locality 2 (NC 039283). Basal breccia of the Stoer Group at Stoer (1 hour). The basal breccia is seen 30m east of the old cemetery at Stoer (NC 041284) (Fig. 49a). Gneiss cobbles and boulders up to 60cm across directly overlie apparently fresh gneiss. They are rounded to sub-angular in shape. The deposit is massive but grades upwards into dark red sandstone with streaks of feldspathic gneiss fragments. This is the base of the type section.

Locality 3 (NC 039283). Stoer Group type section, north shore of Stoer Bay (3 hours). This is a continuation of the type section of the Stoer Group which begins at the previous locality (Figs. 48, 50).

3A. At the eastern end of the section low exposures along high water mark can be easily followed for about 150m before the promontory 3B on Figure 48 is reached. These exposures consist of red siltstone and sandstone beds with a variety of desiccation features and occasional rippled surfaces. The lowest beds contain algal films which perhaps formed in a playa lake. A two-metre bed of coarse pebbly sandstone, exclusively composed of gneiss debris, is a prominent feature of the locality. It can be traced to the north coast of Stoer and southwards into Clachtoll. A thin grey siltstone unit which crops out about half way from the pebbly bed to promontory 3B has a similar lateral persistency and probably represents stagnant conditions at the bottom of a temporarily stratified lake.

3B. Here, a rocky promontory marks the appearance of an entirely new rock unit. It consists of trough cross-bedded red sandstones with well-rounded pebbles, including quartzites (Fig. 49b). Palaeocurrents flowed towards the east. Bedding is occasionally contorted (Fig. 49c). The base of these sandstones, clearly exposed in the promontory, is slightly erosive.

3C. Three couplets each of muddy red sandstone followed by red shale and ripple-marked sandstone interrupt the trough cross-bedded sandstones at 3C (Fig. 48) (NC 035285). Each is several metres thick. One of the couplets contains small cupiferous nodules in its upper part (exposed at low tide) and correlates closely, like its neighbours, with those at Clachtoll, to the south (cf. Locality 1E). The base of the stratigraphically highest muddy sandstone is well seen above the storm beach. It grades downwards over a centimetre or so into the underlying well-sorted sandstone which contains numerous exotic pebbles (Fig. 49d). This is a typical feature of these couplets and suggests that the muddy sandstone represents the climax of a turbid sheet flood which in its early stage had reworked and winnowed the fluvially-deposited sands over which it swept. The overlying thinly bedded red shales and sandstones are interpreted as temporary lake deposits.

3D. The Stac Fada Member. This is a volcanic sandstone 12m thick which has been described as an ash-flow deposit Lawson (1972), as an extrusive peperite (due to the reaction of basic magma with wet sediment at depth) by Sanders and Johnston (1989), and as an originally multi-storey volcanic mudflow deposit by Stewart (1990), and takes its name from the promontory (3D in Fig. 48) which it forms. The rock is essentially similar to the massive muddy sandstone of the couplets described at Loc. 3C, but is packed with much-altered glassy shards up to 10cm across. Gneiss fragments are also present. The member injected and disrupted underlying strata on a grand scale, probably after deposition. Some quite large gneiss blocks which appear at first sight to belong to the underlying strata may have been injected along with matrix in a diluted form, for they lie across the bedding planes and have a seam of debris-flow material around them. The top of the member has been reworked and contains accretionary lapilli. These may be found on the topmost bedding surface which dips into a sand-filled inlet with a waterfall at its head. Knobs of polished rock projecting through the sand at low tide display winnowed seams with whole and broken lapilli. **Do not hammer.**

The glassy shards in the Stac Fada Member have a chemistry which shows them to have been olivine normative and undersaturated, as would be expected if they were the result of rift volcanism. Most of the sodium originally present in the glass, however, has left. Initially the sodium would have helped to generate smectite which, as in the muddy sandstones, probably homogenised the sediment by seasonal expansion and contraction. During later diagenesis, on the conversion of smectite to illite, sodium was remobilised, some going to form the striking albite-microcline-calcite-illite segregations which occur in the Stac Fada Member

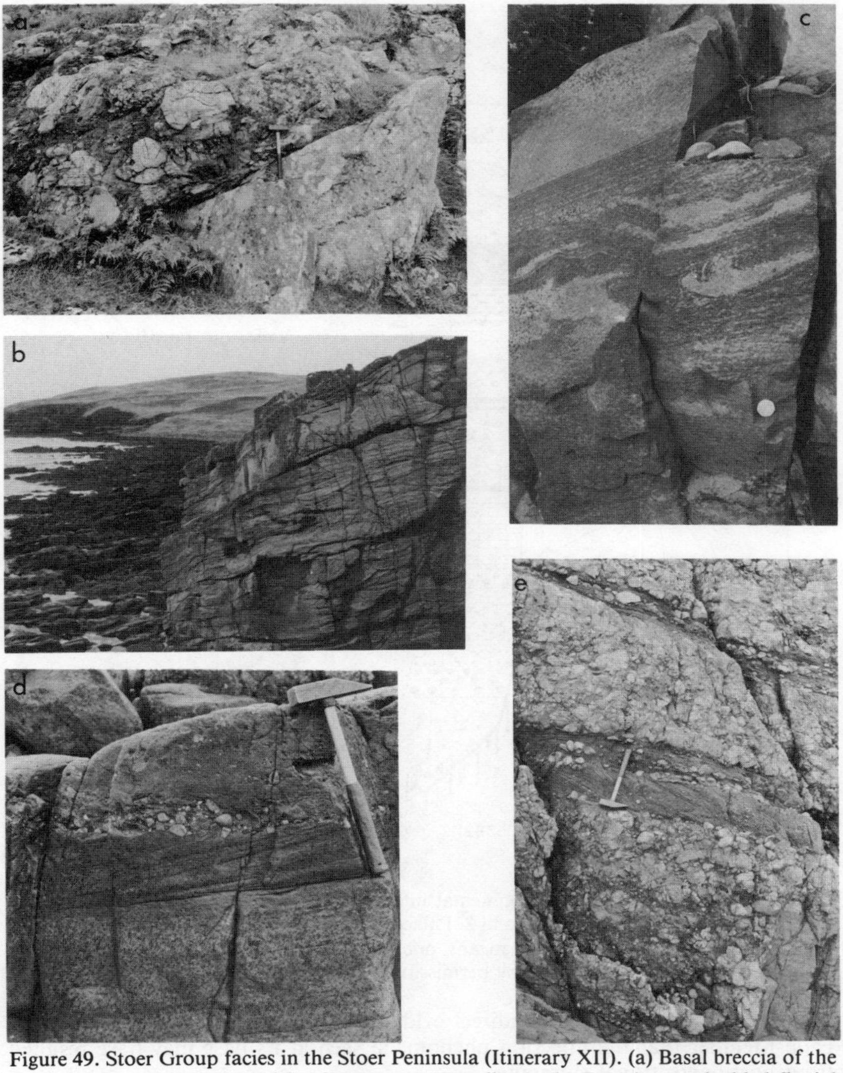

Figure 49. Stoer Group facies in the Stoer Peninsula (Itinerary XII). (a) Basal breccia of the Stoer Group, resting on Lewisian basement at Locality 2. (b) Trough cross-bedded fluvial sandstones, middle part of section at Locality 3B. (c) Contorted bedding in dominantly fluvial middle part of succession at Locality 3B. (d) Trough cross-bedded sandstones with erosional top and overlying sheet flood deposit of conglomerate containing exotic pebbles and muddy sandstone, middle part of succession near Locality 3B. (e) Reinachait Conglomerate at Culkein Bay, Locality 5C; cross-bedded sandstone and gneiss cobble conglomerate of probable fluvial origin.

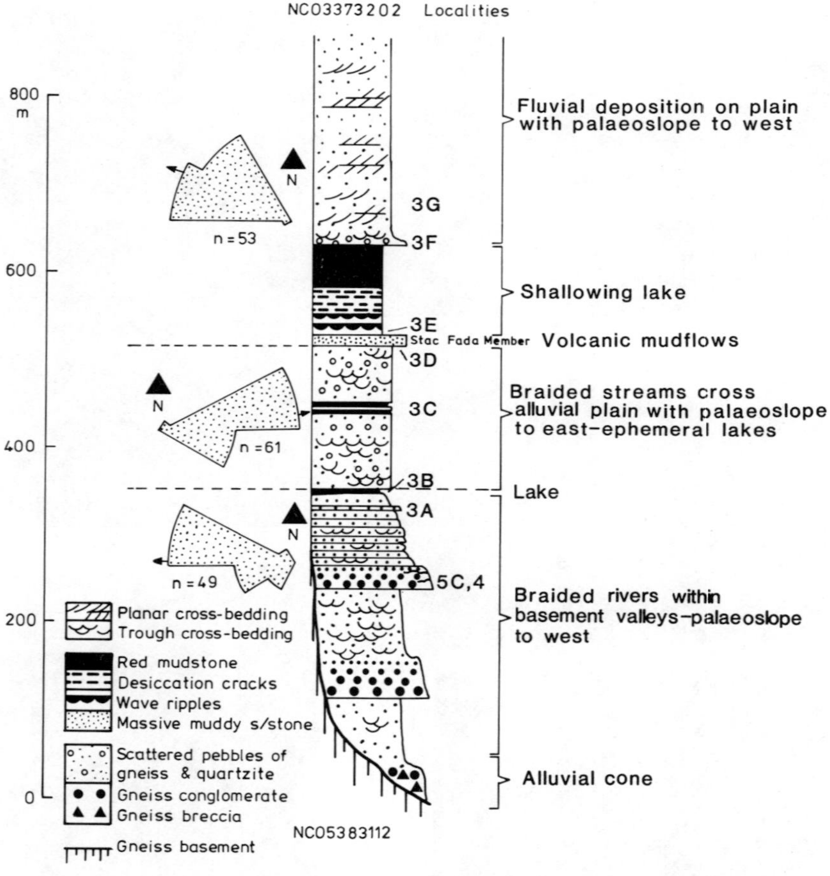

Figure 50. Graphic log and environmental interpretation of the Stoer Group at its type locality, Itinerary XII, Localities 2 and 3. Palaeocurrents from cross-bedding directions are shown as rose diagrams with vector means, one for each of the three intervals identified by dashed lines (from Stewart, 1982, by permission of Blackwell Publications Ltd., Oxford).

at Stoer. It follows from the indirect evidence of abundant smectite in the Stac Fada Member that the injection phenomena seen at its base may have resulted from post-depositional slumping.

3E. After continuing along the cliff top and skirting a small waterfall, descend the low cliff along a slippery bedding plane onto a limestone horizon. The limestone, together with the overlying finely laminated calcareous grey siltstone forms a prominent rib crossing the rough wave-cut platform (3E in Fig. 48). The grey unit is about 2m thick and displays all the characteristics of an oil shale. It probably formed at the bottom of a stratified lake. Above come about 3m of greenish-grey banded siltstones and fine sandstones, some of which are graded. Well-developed calcite pseudomorphs after gypsum up to about 5mm across occur at several levels. These beds are best seen on the walls of the eastern sea cave, accessible at low tide. Microplankton have been reported from the limestone by Downie (1962) and from the grey beds by Cloud & Germs (1971). **Do not hammer the beds at this locality.**

The limestone has been interpreted by Upfold (1984) as stromatolitic but the interpretation has been questioned on the grounds that there are no laterally continuous carbonate sheets, and that the conical carbonate structures described by Upfold lack internal laminae (Janine Sarfati, pers. comm.).

Ascend the cliff and descend again about 90m farther west down another slippery bedding plane to the wave-cut platform. The succession continues that seen at the cave (3E in Fig. 48) and shows an upwards passage from ripple-topped red sandstone through desiccated shaly red siltstones into massive red mudstone.

3F. Walk along the wave-cut platform to the base of the next stratigraphic unit; red sandstones forming an impassable promontory (3F in Fig. 48). The contact can be seen on the cliff. It is perfectly sharp and evidently erosive, for shale fragments are common just above the base. The lowest 4 – 5m of the sandstone are conglomeratic. Pebbles of well-rounded quartzite and gneiss up to 6cm across predominate.

3G. The red sandstones above the conglomerate at (Locality 3F) are best studied near the cliff top (Locality 3G in Fig. 48) and for 100m westward. Pebbles are absent and cross beds form tabular sets about 0.5m thick, frequently separated by ripple-bedded sets. Silt grade material is extremely rare, but where present shows desiccation polygons. Contorted bedding is completely absent. The cross-bedded sandstones were probably deposited as transverse bars in a sluggish river, unlike the trough cross-bedded sandstones beneath the Stac Fada Member which formed in a much more energetic fluvial environment.

Locality 4 (NC 043301). Conglomerate facies in Stoer Group, Reinachait (30 minutes). This is well seen on crags above a gravel pit by the road from Stoer to Culkein. The conglomerate is 12m thick and composed of well-rounded gneiss cobbles. The base of the deposit, not exposed at this locality, is generally sharp. The top grades upwards into red sandstone over a few metres. Stratigraphically above are other conglomerate horizons, similarly graded. This facies does not occur south of Stoer village and seems to represent a fluvial environment rather than the dominantly lacustrine one developed near Clachtoll.

Locality 5 (NC 043327). Stoer Group, north coast of Stoer peninsula (3 hours).

5A. The base of the group is seen on the sea cliff on the south side of the bay at A in Figure 51 (NC 049328). Patches of gneiss breccia overlie a highly irregular gneiss surface. The exposures are easily accessible. The overlying sandstones contain pebbly streaks but are soon replaced by medium-grained sandstones of guite different aspect. These finer sandstones have highly persistent cross-laminae arranged in trough-shaped sets from 0.1 to 10m in thickness. The maximum grain-size is about 3mm. They are tentatively interpreted as aeolian.

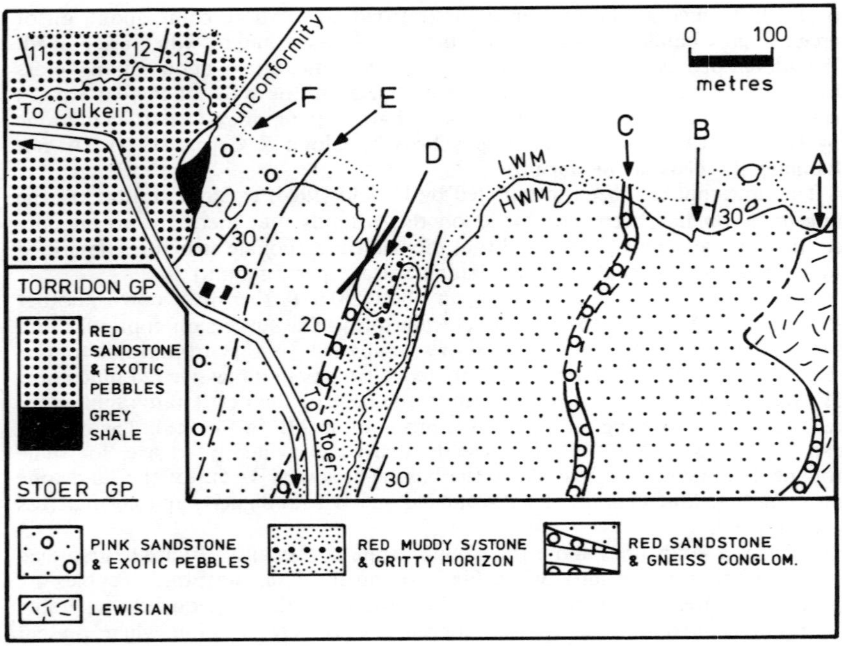

Figure 51. Geological map of Stoer and Torridon groups on the northern coast of the Stoer peninsula, Itinerary XII, Locality 5 (from Stewart 1978, Fig. 9).

5B. Cross-laminated sandstones can be conveniently studied in easily accessible exposures near high water mark at B in Figure 51 (NC 048328). Occasional red shale films along interbeds here have beautiful desiccation 'curls' with polygonal patterns in plan. A thin unit of massive, pebbly sandstone (a flash-flood deposit) at this point rests erosively on the cross-laminated sandstone (probably aeolian). The exposures continue westwards.

5C. The Reinachait Conglomerate reaches the coast at point C (Fig. 49e). The base is strongly erosive and continuously exposed for 50m. The top is sharp and overlain by cross-laminated sandstone. Access is easy from the cliff top.

5D. Cross-laminated sandstones are succeeded by massive muddy sandstone units of very variable thickness with intercalated red shales and limy films, D in Figure 51. A well-sorted gritty horizon which occurs in this section is the 2m bed seen at Locality 3A. The topmost muddy sandstone, which passes up into grey shale, is also seen at Locality 3A.

Trough cross-bedded fine to medium grained red sandstones overlie the muddy sandstones and shales at D (Fig. 51). The boundary is sharp. The sandstones contain very rare pebbles, including quartzite and gneiss and correlate with those at Locality 3B. The exposures are terminated to the west by a cliff face extending out to sea. This cliff is a degraded fault plane, downthrowing to the west. On the cliff face, i.e. the downthrown side, trough cross-bedding gives way upwards to wedge-shaped sets of cross-beds of probable aeolian origin. It is possible to round the promontory and reach the cliff top, but easier to return along the beach to the stream valley at NC 04483279 and walk along the cliff top.

5E. An erosive contact between the cross-laminated facies (below) and fluvial trough cross-bedded sandstones with exotic pebbles is well exposed above high water mark at NC 043329 (E in Fig. 51). The pebbles, up to 2cm in size, include gneiss and quartzite. Contorted bedding and overturned cross-bedding are common in the sandstones above the erosion surface.

5F. The unconformity with the Torridon Group is seen in the floor of a small bay at low tide (F in Fig. 51). Up to 10m of predominantly red Diabaig siltstones overlie an irregular surface cut in the Stoer Group. Blocks of Stoer Group sandstone up to a metre across are present in the Diabaig Formation immediately above the unconformity. Diabaig siltstones are also seen above high water mark on the south side of the bay. The Diabaig Formation shows occasional rippled surfaces and desiccation cracks. It is erosively overlain by very coarse Applecross sandstones with the typical exotic pebble suite. These coarse sandstones cut out the Diabaig Formation to the north and come to rest directly on the Stoer Group (NC 04243301). This part of the unconformity can be seen at any time except high tide. The angular nature of the unconformity is clear.

REFERENCES

ALLISON, I., F. MAY & R. A. STRACHAN 1988. *An Excursion Guide to the Moine Geology of the Scottish Highlands.* Scottish Academic Press, 270pp.

ANDERSON, F. W. & K. C. DUNHAM 1966. *The geology of northern Skye. Explanation of the Portree (80) and parts of the Rubha Hunish (90), Applecross (81) and Gairloch (91) Sheets.* Mem. geol. Surv., Scotland, 216pp.

ANDERTON, R. 1975. Tidal flat and shallow marine sediments from the Craignish Phyllites, Middle Dalradian, Argyll, Scotland. *Geol. Mag.,* 112, 337-48.

ANDERTON, R. 1976. Tidal shelf sedimentation: an example from the Scottish Dalradian. *Sedimentology,* 23, 429-58.

ANDERTON, R. 1977. The Dalradian rocks of Jura. *Scott J. Geol.,* 13, 135-42.

ANDERTON, R. 1979. Slopes, submarine fans and syn-depositional faults: sedimentology of parts of the Middle and Upper Dalradian in the SW Highlands of Scotland. *In:* HARRIS, A. L., C. H. HOLLAND & B. E. LEAKE (eds.) *The Caledonides of the British Isles–reviewed.* Geol. Soc. Lond. Spec. Publ., 8, 483-8.

ANDERTON, R. 1982. Dalradian deposition and the late Precambrian-Cambrian history of the N Atlantic region: a review of the early evolution of the Iapetus ocean. *Jl. geol. Soc. Lond.,* 139, 421-31.

ANDERTON, R. 1985. Sedimentation and tectonics in the Scottish Dalradian. *Scott. J. Geol.,* 21, 407-36.

BAILEY, E. B. & H. B. MAUFE 1916. *The Geology of Ben Nevis and Glencoe and the Surrounding Country. Explanation of Sheet 53.* Mem. geol. Surv. Scotland.

BAILEY, E. B. & W. J. McCALLIEN 1937. Perthshire tectonics. Schiehallion to Glen Lyon. *Trans r. Soc. Edinb.,* 59, 79-117.

BAIRD, A. W. 1982. The Sgurr Beag Slide within Moine rocks at Loch Eilt, Inverness-shire. *Jl. geol. Soc. Lond.,* 139, 647-53.

BALDWIN, C. T. & H. D. JOHNSON 1977. The Dalradian rocks of Lunga, Luing and Shuna. *Scott. J. Geol.,* 13, 143-54.

BARBER, A. J., A. BEACH, R. G. PARK, J. TARNEY & A. D. STEWART 1978. *The Lewisian and Torridonian of North-West Scotland.* Geol. Ass. Guide No. 21, 99pp.

BARR, D., A. M. ROBERTS, A. J. HIGHTON, L. M. PARSON & A. L. HARRIS 1985. Structural setting and geochronological significance of the West Highland Granitic Gneiss, a deformed early granite within Proterozoic Moine rocks of NW Scotland. *Jl. geol. Soc. Lond.,* 142, 663-75.

BORRADAILE, G. J. & H. D. JOHNSON 1973. Finite strain estimates from the Dalradian Dolomitic Formation, Islay, Argyll, Scotland. *Tectonophysics,* 18, 249-59.

BOWES, D. R. 1968. The absolute time scale and the subdivision of Precambrian rocks in Scotland. *Geol. Foren. Stockholm Forh.,* 90, 175-88.

BRADBURY, H. J., R. A. SMITH & A. L. HARRIS 1976. 'Older' granites as time-markers in Dalradian evolution. *Jl. geol. Soc. Lond.,* 132, 677-84.

BROOK, M., D. POWELL & M. S. BREWER 1976. Grenville age for rocks in the Moine of north-western Scotland. *Nature,* 260, 515-7.

BROWN, G. C. & C. A. LOCKE 1979. Space-time variations in British Caledonian granites: some geophysical correlations. *Earth planet. Sci. Lett.,* 45, 69-79.

CLOUD, P. & A. GERMS 1971. New Pre-Paleozoic nannofossils from the Stoer Formation (Torridonian), northwest Scotland. *Bull. geol. Soc. Am.,* 82 3469-74.

CRAIG, G. Y. (ed.) 1983. *Geology of Scotland.* 2nd edn. Scottish Academic Press, Edinburgh, 472 p.

DEWEY, J. F. & R. M. SHACKLETON 1984. A model for the evolution of the Grampian tract in the early Caledonides and Appalachians. *Nature,* 312, 115-121.

DeRAAF, J. F. M., J. R. BOERSMA & A. van GELDER 1977. Wave-generated structures and sequences from a shallow marine succession, Lower Carboniferous, County Cork, Ireland. *Sedimentology,* 24, 451-83.

DOWNIE, C. 1962. Demonstration of so-called spores from the Torridonian. *Proc. geol. Soc. Lond.,* 1600, 127-8.

EYLES, C. H. 1989. Glacially- and tidally-influenced shallow marine sedimentation of the Late Precambrian Port Askaig Formation, Scotland. *Palaeogeog., Palaeoclimatol., Palaeoecol.,* 68, 1-25.

EYLES, N. & B. M. CLARK 1985. Gravity-induced soft-sediment deformation in glaciomarine sequences of the Upper Proterozoic Port Askaig Formation, Scotland, *Sedimentology,* 32, 789-814.

EYLES, C. H. & N. EYLES 1983. Glaciomarine model for upper Precambrian diamictites of the Port Askaig Formation, Scotland. *Geology,* 11, 692-6.

EYLES, C. H., N. EYLES & A. D. MIALL 1985. Models of glaciomarine sedimentation and their application to the interpretation of ancient glacial sequences. *Palaeogeol., Palaeoclimatol., Palaeoecol.,* 51, 51-84.

FAIRCHILD, I. J. 1977. Phengite spherules from the Dalradian Bonahaven Formation, Islay, Scotland: glauconitized microfossils? *Geol. Mag.,* 114, 355-64.

FAIRCHILD, I. J. 1978. *Sedimentation and post-depositional history of the Dalradian Bonahaven Formation of Islay.* Unpubl. PhD thesis, Univ. of Nottingham.

FAIRCHILD, I. J. 1980a. Sedimentation and origin of a late Precambrian 'dolomite' from Scotland. *J. sediment. Petrol.,* 50, 423-46.

FAIRCHILD, I. J. 1980b. Stages in Precambrian dolomitization, Scotland: cementing versus replacement textures. *Sedimentology,* 27, 631-50.

FAIRCHILD., I. J. 1980c. The structure of NE Islay. Scott. J. Geol., 16, 189-99.

FAIRCHILD, I. J. 1985a. Comment on 'Glaciomarine model for upper Precambrian diamictites of the Port Askaig Formation, Scotland,' *Geology,* 13, 89-90.

FAIRCHILD, I. J. 1985b. Petrography and carbonate chemistry of some Dalradian dolomitic metasediments: preservation of diagenetic textures. *Jl. geol. Soc. Lond.,* 142, 167-85.

FAIRCHILD, I. J. 1989. Dolomitic stromatolite-bearing units with storm deposits from the Vendian of East Greenland and Scotland: a case of facies equivalence. *In:* GAYER, R. A. (ed.), *Caledonian and Related Geology of Scandinavia,* Graham & Trotman, London, 275-83.

FAIRCHILD, I. J. & M. J. HAMBREY 1984. The Vendian of northeastern Spitsbergen: petrogenesis of a dolomite-tillite association. *Precambrian. Res.,* 26, 111-67.

FAIRCHILD, I. J. & P. M. HERRINGTON 1989. A tempestite-stromatolite-evaporite association (late Vendian, East Greenland): a shoreface-lagoon model. *Precambrian Res.,* 43, 101-27.

FERMOR, L. L. 1951. On a discovery of copper-ore in the Torridonian rocks of Sutherland. *Geol. Mag.,* 88, 215-8.

FETTES, D & R. MACDONALD 1978. Glen Garry vein complex. *Scott J. Geol.,* 14, 335-58.

FITCHES, W. R. & A. J. MALTMAN 1984. Tectonic development and stratigraphy at the western margin of the Caledonides: Islay and Colonsay, Scotland. *Trans. r. Soc. Edinb., Earth Sci.,* 75, 365-82.

GEIKIE, A. 1900. *Summ. Prog. geol. Surv. G.B. for 1899.* London.

GLOVER, B. W. & J. A. WINCHESTER 1989. The Grampian Group: a major Late Proterozoic clastic sequence in the Central Highlands of Scotland. *Jl. geol. Soc. Lond.,* 146, 85-96.

GOWER, P. J. 1977. The Dalradian rocks of the west coast of the Tayvallich peninsula. *Scott. J. Geol.,* 13, 125-33.

GRACIE, A. J. & A. D. STEWART 1967. Torridonian sediments at Enard Bay, Ross-shire. *Scott. J. Geol.,* 3, 181-94.

GRAHAM, C. M. 1986. The role of the Cruachan Lineament during Dalradian evolution. *Scott. J. Geol.,* 22, 257-70.

HALL, A. J. 1982. Gypsum as a precursor to pyrrhotite in metamorphic rocks. *Mineral Deposits,* 17, 401-9.

HALLIDAY, A. N., C. M. GRAHAM, M. AFTALION & P. DYMOKE 1989. The depositional age of the Dalradian Supergroup: U-Pb and Sm-Nd isotopic studies of the Tayvallich Volcanics, Scotland. *Jl. geol. Soc. Lond.,* 146, 3-6.

HAMBREY, M. J. 1983. Correlation of Late Proterozoic tillites in the North Atlantic region and Europe. *Geol. Mag.,* 120, 209-32.

HAMBREY, M. J. & W. B. HARLAND (eds.) 1981. *Earth's pre-Pleistocene Glacial Record,* Cambridge Univ. Press, xv, 1004pp.

HAMBREY, M. J. & W. B. HARLAND, 1985. The Late Proterozoic glacial era. *Palaeogeog., Palaeoclimatol., Palaeoecol.,* 51, 255-72.

HARRIS, A. L., C. T. BALDWIN, H. J. BRADBURY, H. D. JOHNSON & R. A. SMITH 1978. Ensialic basin sedimentation: the Dalradian Supergroup. *In:* BOWES, D. R. & B. E. LEAKE (eds.) *Crustal evolution in northwestern Britain and adjacent areas.* Geol. Soc. Lond. Spec. Issue, 10, 115-38.

HAY, S. J., J. HALL, G. SIMMONS & M. J. RUSSELL 1988. Sealed microcracks in the Lewisian of NW Scotland: a record of 2 billion years of fluid circulation. *Jl. geol. Soc. Lond.,* 145, 819-30.

HOLDSWORTH, R. E., A. L. HARRIS & A. M. ROBERTS 1987. The stratigraphy, structure and regional significance of the Moine rocks of Mull, Argyllshire, W. Scotland. *Geol. J.,* 22, 83-107.

HICKMAN, A. 1975. The stratigraphy of the Late Precambrian metasediments between Glen Roy and Lismore. *Scott. J. Geol.,* 11, 117-42.

IRVING, D. & S. K. RUNCORN 1957. Analysis of the palaeomagnetism of the Torridonian Sandstone Series of north-west Scotland. *Phil. Trans. r. Soc.,* A 250, 83-99.

IUGS (International Union of Geological Sciences) 1989. Global stratigraphic chart. Supplement to *Episodes,* 19(2).

JOHNSON, M. R. W. 1983a. Dalradian. *In*: CRAIG, G. Y. (ed.) *Geology of Scotland.* 2nd edn. Scottish Academic Press, Edinburgh, 77-104.

JOHNSON, M. R. W. 1983b. Torridonian-Moine. *In*: CRAIG, G. Y. (ed.) *Geology of Scotland.* 2nd edn. Scottish Academic Press, Edinburgh, 49-75.

JOHNSON, M. R. W. & I. PARSONS 1979. *Macgregor and Phemister's Geological Excursion Guide to the Assynt District of Sutherland.* Edinb. geol. Soc., Edinburgh, 76p.

JOHNSTONE, G. S., D. I. SMITH & A. L. HARRIS 1969. The Moinian Assemblage of Scotland. *Am. Assoc. Petrol. Geol. Mem.,* 12, 159-80.

KELLING, G., W. E. A. PHILLIPS, A. L. HARRIS & M. F. HOWELLS 1985. The Caledonides of the British Isles: a review and appraisal. *In*: GEE, D. G. & B. A. STURT (eds.) *The Caledonide Orogen – Scandinavia and related areas.* Wiley, Chichester, 1125-46.

KENNEDY, W. Q. 1946. The Great Glen Fault. *Quart. Jl. geol. Soc. Lond.,* 102, 41-76.

KENNEDY, W. Q. 1949. Zones of progressive regional metamorphism in the Moine Schists of the Western Highlands. *Geol. Mag.,* 86, 43-56.

KESSLER, L. G. & I. G. GOLLOP 1988. Inner shelf/shoreface-intertidal transition, Upper Precambrian, Port Askaig Tillite, Isle of Islay, Argyll, Scotland. *In*: de BOER, P. L., A. van GELDER & S. D. NIO (eds.) *Tide-influenced Sedimentary Environments and Facies,* Reidel, Dordrecht, 341-58.

KILBURN, C., W. S. PITCHER & R. M. SHACKLETON 1965. The stratigraphy and origin of the Port Askaig Boulder Bed Series (Dalradian). *Geol. Jl.,* 4, 343-60.

KLEIN, G. de V. 1970. Tidal origin of a Precambrian quartzite: the Lower Fine-grained Quartzite of Islay. *J. sediment. Petrol.,* 40, 973-85.

LAMBERT, R. St. J. 1969. Isotopic studies relating to the Precambrian history of the Moinian of Scotland. *Proc. geol. Soc. Lond.,* 1652, 243-5.

LAWSON, D. E. 1972. Torridonian volcanic sediments. *Scott. J. Geol.,* 8, 345-62.

McCAVE, I. N. 1971. Discussion of 'Tidal origin of a Precambrian quartzite: the Lower Fine-grained Quartzite of Islay' by G. de V. Klein. *J. Sediment. Petrol.,* 41, 1159-50.

MOORBATH, S. 1969. Evidence of the age of deposition in the Torridonian sediments of north-west Scotland. *Scott. J. Geol.,* 5, 154-70.

PARK, R. G. & J. TARNEY 1987. The Lewisian Complex: a typical Precambrian high-grade terrane? *In*: PARK, R. G. & J. TARNEY (eds.) *Evolution of the Lewisian and Comparable High-grade Terranes.* Spec. Publ. geol. Soc. Lond., 27, 13-35.

PEAT, C. & W. DIVER 1982. First signs of life on Earth. *New Scientist,* 95, 776-81.

PIASECKI, M. A. J. 1980. New light on the Moine rocks of the Central Highlands of Scotland. *Jl. geol. Soc. Lond.,* 137, 41-59.

PIASECKI, M. A. J. & O. van BREEMEN 1979. The 'Central Highland Granulites': cover-basement tectonics in the Moine. *In:* HARRIS, A. L., C. H. HOLLAND & B. E. LEAKE (eds.) *The Caledonides of the British Isles–reviewed.* Geol. Soc. Lond. Spec. Publ., 8, 139-44.

PIASECKI, M. A. J. & O. van BREEMEN 1983. Field and isotopic evidence for a c. 750 Ma tectonothermal event in Moine rocks in the Central Highland region of the Scottish Caledonides. *Trans. r. Soc. Edinb.,* 73, 119-34.

POWELL, D., A. W. BAIRD, N. R. CHARNLEY & P. J. JORDAN 1981. The metamorphic environment of the Sgurr Beag Slide: a major crustal displacement zone in Proterozoic, Moine rocks of Scotland. *Jl. geol. Soc. Lond.,* 138, 661-73.

PRINGLE, J. R. 1973. Rb-Sr age determinations on shales associated with the Varanger Ice Age. *Geol. Mag.,* 109, 465-72.

RAMSAY, J. G. 1969. The measurement of strain and displacement in orogenic belts. *In*: KENT, P. E., G. E. SATTERTHWAITE & A. M. SPENCER *Time and Place in Orogeny.* Spec. Publ. geol. Soc. Lond., 3, 13-79.

ROBERTS, J. L. 1976. The structure of the Dalradian rocks in the N Ballachulish district of Scotland. *JL. geol. Soc. Lond.,* 132, 139-54.

ROBERTS, J. L. 1977. The Dalradian rocks of Knapdale and North Kintyre. *Scott. J. Geol.,* 13, 113-24.

ROBERTS, J. L. & J. E. TREAGUS 1977a. The Dalradian rocks of the Loch Leven area. *Scott. J. Geol.,* 13, 165-84.

ROBERTS, J. L. & J. E. TREAGUS 1977b. Polyphase generation of nappe structures in the Dalradian of the SW Highlands of Scotland. *Scott. J. Geol.,* 13, 237-54.

ROBERTS, A. M., R. A. STRACHAN, A. L. HARRIS, D. BARR & R. E. HOLDSWORTH 1987. The Sgurr Beag nappe: a reassessment of the stratigraphy and structure of the Northern Highland Moine. *Bull. geol. Soc. Am.,* 98, 497-506.

ROGERS, G., T. J. DEMSTER, B. J. BLUCK & P. W. G. TANNER 1989. A high precision U-Pb age for the Ben Vuirich granite: implications for the evolution of the Scottish Dalradian Supergroup. *Jl. geol. Soc. Lond.,* 146, 789-98.

SANDERS I. S. & J. D. JOHNSTON 1989. The Torridonian Stac Fada Member: an extrusion of fluidised peperite? *Trans. r. Soc. Edinb., Earth Sciences,* 80, 1-4.

SCHERMERHORN, L. J. G. 1974. Late Precambrian mixtites: glacial and/or non-glacial? *Am. J. Sci.,* 274, 673-824.

SCHERMERHORN, L. J. G. 1975. Tectonic framework of Late Precambrian supposed glacials. *In*: WRIGHT, A. E. & F. MOSELEY (eds.) *Ice ages: Ancient and Modern,* Seel House Press, Liverpool, 242-74.

SELLEY, R. C. 1965. Diagnostic characters of fluviatile sediments of the Torridonian formation (Precambrian) of north-west Scotland. *J. sediment. Petrol.,* 35, 366-80.

SELLEY, R. C. 1966. Petrography of the Torridonian rocks of Raasay and Scalpay, Inverness-shire. *Proc. Geol. Ass.,* 77, 293-314.

SELLEY, R. C. 1969. Torridonian alluvium and quicksands. *Scott. J. Geol.,* 5, 328-46.

SELLEY, R. C., D. J. SHEARMAN, J. SUTTON & J. WATSON 1963. Some underwater disturbances on the Torridonian of Skye and Raasay. *Geol. Mag.,* 100, 224-43.

SMITH, D. I. 1979. Caledonian minor intrusions of the N Highlands of Scotland. *In*: Harris, A. L., C. H. Holland & B. E. Leake (eds.) *The Caledonides of the British Isles—reviewed.* Geol. Soc. Lond. Spec. Publ., 8, 863-97.

SMITH, R. L., J. E. F. STEARN & J. D. A. PIPER 1983. Palaeomagnetic studies on the Torridonian sediments, NW Scotland. *Scott. J. Geol.,* 19, 29-45.

SPENCER, A. M. 1971a. *Late Precambrian glaciation in Scotland.* Mem. geol. Soc. Lond., 6, 100p.

SPENCER, A. M. 1971b. Discussion of 'Tidal origin of a Precambrian quartzite: the Lower Fine-grained Quartzite of Islay' by G. de V. Klein. *J. sediment. Petrol.,* 41, 884-5.

SPENCER, A. M. 1975. Late Precambrian glaciation in the North Atlantic region. *In*: WRIGHT, A. E. & F. MOSELEY (eds.) *Ice ages: Ancient and Modern,* Seel House Press, Liverpool, 217-40.

SPENCER, A. M. 1985. Mechanisms and environments of deposition of Late Precambrian geosynclinal tillites: Scotland and East Greenland. *Palaeogeog., Palaeoclimatol., Palaeoecol.,* 51, 143-57.

SPENCER, A. M. & M. O. SPENCER 1972. The late Precambrian/Lower Cambrian Bonahaven Dolomite of Islay and its stromatolites. *Scott. J. Geol.,* 8, 269-82.

STEWART, A. D. 1962. On the Torridonian sediments of Colonsay and their relationship to the main outcrop in north-west Scotland. *Liverpool Manchester geol. J.,* 3, 121-56.

STEWART, A. D. 1963. On certain slump structures in the Torridonian sandstones of Applecross. *Geol. Mag.,* 100, 205-218.

STEWART, A. D. 1966a. An unconformity in the Torridonian. *Geol. Mag.,* 103, 462-5.

STEWART, A. D. 1966b. On the correlation of the Torridonian between Rhum and Skye. *Geol. Mag.,* 103, 432-9.

STEWART, A. D. 1975. 'Torridonian' rocks of western Scotland. In: HARRIS, A. L. et al. *A Correlation of the Precambrian rocks in the British Isles.* Spec. Publ. geol. Soc. Lond., No. 6, 43-51.

STEWART, A. D. 1982. Late Proterozoic rifting in NW Scotland: the genesis of the 'Torridonian'. *Jl. geol. Soc. Lond.,* 139, 413-9.

STEWART, A. D. 1988a. The Sleat and Torridon groups. In: Winchester, J. A. (ed.) *Later Proterozoic Stratigraphy of the Northern Atlantic Regions.* Blackie, Glasgow, 104-12.

STEWART, A. D. 1988b. The Stoer Group, Scotland. In: Winchester, J. A. (ed.) *Later Proterozoic Stratigraphy of the Northern Atlantic Regions.* Blackie, Glasgow, 97-103.

STEWART, A. D. 1990. Geochemistry, provenance and climate of the Upper Proterozoic Stoer Group in Scotland. *Scott. J. Geol.,* in press.

STEWART, A. D. & B. D. HACKMAN 1973. Precambrian sediments of western Islay. *Scott. J. Geol.,* 9, 185-201.

STEWART, A. D. & E. IRVING 1974. Palaeomagnetism of Precambrian sedimentary rocks from NW Scotland and the apparent polar wandering path of Laurentia. *Geophys. J. r. Astr. Soc.,* 37, 51-72.

STEWART, A. D. & A. PARKER 1979. Palaeosalinity and environmental interpretation of red beds from the late Precambrian ('Torridonian') of Scotland. *Sediment. Geol.,* 22, 229-41.

STRACHAN, R. A. 1982. Tectonic sliding within the Moinian Loch Eil Division near Kinlocheil, W. Inverness-shire. *Scott. J. Geol.,* 18, 187-203.

STRACHAN, R. A. 1985. The stratigraphy and structure of the Moine rocks of the Loch Eil area, Inverness-shire. *Scott. J. Geol.,* 21, 9-22.

STRACHAN, R. A. 1986. Shallow marine sedimentation in the Proterozoic Moine Succession, Northern Scotland. *Precambrian Res.,* 32, 17-33.

SUTTON, J. & J. WATSON 1960. Sedimentary structures in the Epidotic Grits of Skye. *Geol. Mag.,* 97, 106-22.

SUTTON, J. & J. WATSON 1964. Some aspects of Torridonian stratigraphy in Skye. *Proc. Geol. Ass.,* 75, 251-87.

THOMAS, P. R. 1980. The stratigraphy and structure of the Moine rocks of the Schiehallion Complex, Scotland. *Jl. geol. Soc. Lond.,* 137, 469-82.

TANNER, P. W. G. 1970. The Sgurr Beag Slide – a major tectonic break within the Moinian of the western Highlands of Scotland. *Quart. Jl. geol. Soc. Lond.,* 126, 435-63.

TREAGUS, J. E. 1969. The Kinlochlaggan Boulder Bed. *Proc. geol. Soc. Lond.,* 1654, 55-60.

TREAGUS, J. E. 1974. A structural cross-section of the Moine and Dalradian rocks of the Kinlochleven area, Scotland. *Jl. geol. Soc. Lond.,* 130, 525-44.

TREAGUS, J. E. 1981. The Lower Dalradian Kinlochlaggan Boulder Bed, central Scotland. *In*: HAMBREY, M. J. & W. B. HARLAND (eds.) *Earth's pre-Pleistocene Glacial Record.* Cambridge Univ. Press, Cambridge. 637-9.

TREAGUS, J. E. 1987. The structural evolution of the Dalradian of the Central Highlands of Scotland. *Trans r. Soc. Edinb., Earth Sci.,* 78, 1-15.

TREAGUS, J. E. & G. KING 1978. A complete Lower Dalradian succession in the Schiehallion district, Central Perthshire. *Scott. J. Geol.,* 14, 157-66.

UPFOLD, R. L. 1984. Tufted microbial (cyanobacterial) mats from the Proterozoic Stoer Group, Scotland. *Geol. Mag.,* 121, 351-55.

VAN BREEMEN, O., R. T. PIDGEON & M. R. W. JOHNSON 1974. Precambrian and Palaeozoic pegmatites in the Moines of Northern Scotland. *Jl. geol. Soc. Lond.,* 130, 493-507.

VAN DER VOO, R. & C. SCOTESE 1981. Paleomagnetic evidence for a large (2000km) sinistral offset along the Great Glen Fault during Carboniferous time. *Geology,* 9, 583-9.

WALTER, M. R. 1972. Stromatolites and the biostratigraphy of the Australian Precambrian and Cambrian. *Spec. Pap. Palaeont.,* 11, 1-190.

WILLIAMS, G. E. 1969a. Petrography and origin of pebbles from Torridonian strata (late Precambrian), north-west Scotland. In North Atlantic Geology and Continental Drift. *Mem. Am. Ass. Petrol. Geol.,* 12, 609-29.

WILLIAMS, G. E. 1969b. Characteristics and origin of a Precambrian pediment. *J. Geol.,* 77, 183-207.

WINCHESTER, J. A. 1973. Pattern of regional metamorphism suggests a sinistral displacement of 160km along the Great Glen Fault. *Nature Phys. Sci.,* 246, 81-4.

WINCHESTER, J. A. 1974. The zonal patten of regional metamorphism in the Scottish Caledonides. *Jl. geol. Soc. Lond.,* 130, 509-24.

WINCHESTER, J. A. 1984. The geochemistry of the Strathconon amphibolites, Northern Scotland. *Scott. J. Geol.,* 20, 37-51.

WINCHESTER, J. A. 1985. Major low-angle fault displacement measured by matching amphibolite chemistry – an example from Scotland. *Geology,* 13, 604-6.

WINCHESTER, J. A. (ed.) *Later Proterozoic Stratigraphy of the Northern Atlantic Regions.* Blackie, Glasgow, 279p.

ZHANG, Z. 1982. Upper Proterozoic microfossils from the Summer Isles, N.W. Scotland. *Palaeontology.* 25, 443-60.

ZHANG, Z., W. L. DIVER & P. R. GRANT 1981. Microfossils from the Aultbea Formation, Torridon Group, on Tanera Beg, Summer Isles. *Scott. J. Geol.,* 17, 149-53.

INDEX